The POPULAR
MECHANICS

ILLUSTRATED HOME

HANDYMAN

ENCYCLOPEDIA & GUIDE

EDITED BY THE STAFF OF POPULAR MECHANICS

J. J. Little & Ives Co., Inc., New York — 1961

Plastic case designed for Mercury II camera can be used with other cameras when controls are relocated

TAKE YOUR CAMERA UNDERWATER

By Hampden Banks, Jr.

WITH YOUR 35-mm. camera in this watertight plastic case you can photograph marine life in black-and-white or color just as easily as taking pictures on land. The case described in this article is designed for a Mercury II camera, because this model enables one to take 72 split-frame pictures on a 36-exposure roll without disassembling the case to reload. However, almost any 35-mm. camera can be used simply by relocating the controls.

When making the case, first cut the sides, ends, top and bottom from ½-in. plastic and machine to size, leaving the protective paper on the material to prevent scarring its surface. After grooving the inner surfaces of the ends as shown in Figs. 1 and 2, for positioning the camera, the sides, ends and top are cemented together. When cementing two pieces of plastic, the interfaces need not be polished. It is sufficient to sand the machined edges only with No. 400 grit sandpaper. If clamps are used, they should be pulled up not too tightly, to permit the cement to spread evenly. When applying cement, use an eye dropper. A well-cemented joint is completely transparent.

Next, a rectangle is cut from ¼-in. plastic to fit snugly inside the bottom of the case. This piece, when cemented to the bottom member of the case, serves as a base plate for the camera and provides for proper

1601

positioning and clearance for the camera controls. After drilling the bolt hole in the base assembly, it is counterbored ³⁄₁₆ in. deep to accept two rubber gaskets and the head of the camera-clamping screw, after which the camera is bolted in place. Four ¼ x ⁵⁄₁₆-in. plastic guides are then cemented to the base plate as shown in Fig. 1, to aid in positioning the camera each time it is placed in the case.

Assemblies for Camera Controls

The brass fittings for the film-advance, shutter-cock and shutter-speed controls are cut and machined from brass tubing and rod as required and the gears silver-soldered to them as shown in Fig. 4, detail C. The brass collar for the film advance is machined to provide a press fit directly on the camera knob, while the shutter-speed control merely replaces the original knob on the camera.

When making the metal collar for the aperture control, Fig. 3, detail E, the f-numbers and calibrations should be re-produced on a strip of paper and glued on the collar after the latter is positioned properly over the lens barrel with the pin and offset control rod attached. Then, the small knob on the camera body used for focusing is tapped and a control rod, the same as the one used for the aperture control, screwed to it. Next, control-knob holes are machined in the front and one end of the case as shown in Fig. 4, detail B, and all plastic control-knob fittings are machined and polished. When drilling, tapping, milling or turning plastic, use liberal amounts of kerosene for lubricating it. After the rubber gaskets are cut from a piece of inner tube about ¹⁄₁₆ in. thick, holes for fastening the cover plates are tapped, and parts for the controls made as shown in Figs. 2 and 3, after which each control is assembled and inserted in its respective hole in the case. When the inside assemblies are completed as shown in the details, each is secured to the shaft cut for it, Fig. 4, detail D. Also, the focus and lens-aperture controls are connected to

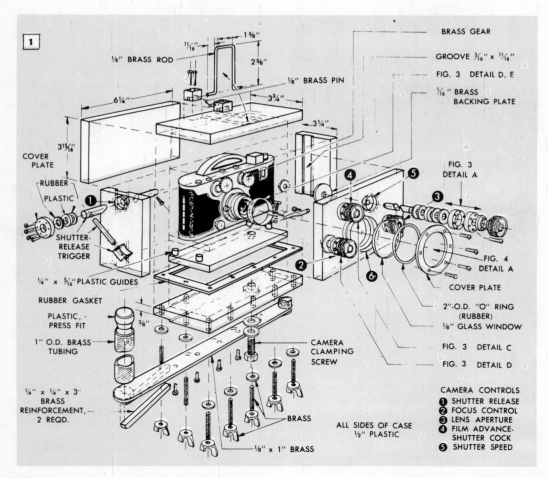

When inserting camera in case, be sure trigger-release screw is out of way and gears mesh, then secure base with wing nuts

latter to be disengaged for unobstructed action of the shutter-gear train.

When satisfied that all controls work smoothly, cement the plastic disk in position on each shaft so the rubber gaskets fit flush in their chamber after the gaskets are coated with silicone grease and secured by the cover plate. All parts for the controls are made from plastic stock except the gaskets, control rods, aperture-control collar and gear parts.

Lens-Cover Plate

For a watertight installation of the lens-cover plate, machine the aperture accurately to the specifications shown in Fig. 4, detail A, and screw the parts into position. The "0" ring needs no silicone grease. It is wise to keep this grease away from parts to be cemented since presence of the material will prevent a bond between surfaces.

To accommodate the $\frac{1}{8}$ x 1 x $10\frac{7}{16}$-in. length of flat brass to which the reinforcement bars and handles are silver-soldered, the camera is removed from the base plate and a rabbet is cut in the bottom member,

their respective controls on the camera and checked for proper alignment at this time. The outside assemblies are the same for all controls except that a trigger-release arm is used in place of a knob on control No. 1. Only one rubber gasket is required on each side of the plastic disk for controls 1, 2, 3 and 4, and the plastic chamber extension is needed on the shutter-speed control only. This is necessary to permit the gears on the

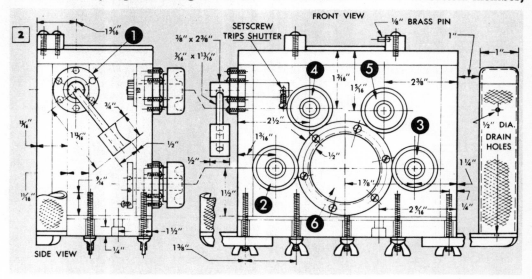

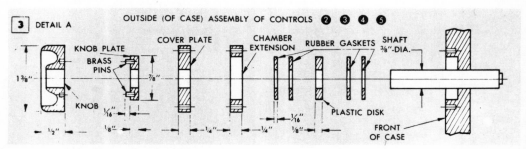

Fig. 1. The handle assembly is then screwed to the bottom and holes for securing the latter to the case are drilled, spaced 1⅜ in. on center as shown in Figs. 1 and 2. The holes drilled in the vertical members of the case are tapped to receive 1½-in. studs cut from 8-32-threaded brass rod. The studs are then coated with cement and screwed in position. A rubber gasket cut from an inner tube and coated with silicone grease on both sides provides a watertight seal when the bottom is screwed in place. When fastening the bottom, only moderate pressure should be applied on the wing nuts, tightening those at the center first and working outward. The grease on the gasket will appear to change color when a watertight seal is made. If the case is not to be used for a time, the cover-plate screws should be loosened to prevent slow seepage of the grease out of the fittings.

The design of the plastic case provides for a slight buoyancy for easier operation of the camera. If no buoyancy is desired, the hollow handles may be filled with small pieces of brass, copper or stainless steel. ★ ★ ★

Right, view finder mounted on ⅝ x ⅞-in. plastic screwed to top of case folds flat when not in use

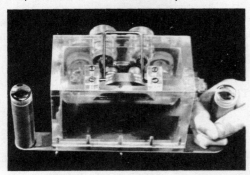

Above, after brass gears are silver-soldered to appropriate fittings for film advance and speed controls, the latter two are installed in place of knobs

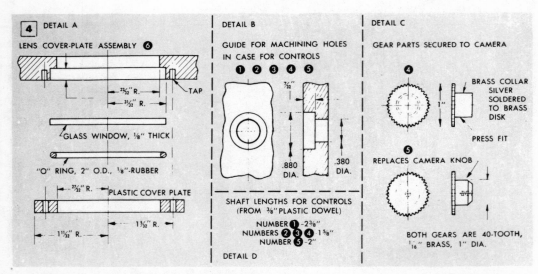

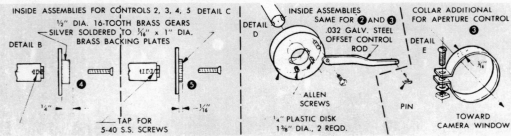

ENLARGING 8 MM FILMS

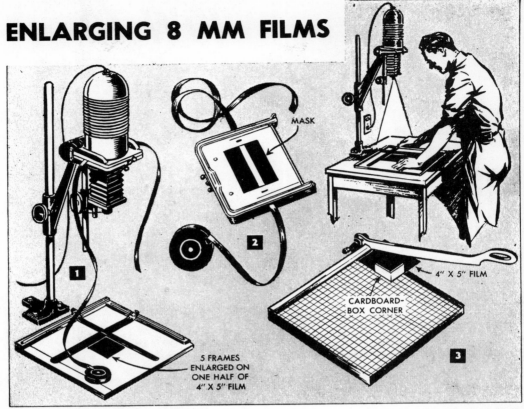

MASK

5 FRAMES ENLARGED ON ONE HALF OF 4" X 5" FILM

4" X 5" FILM

CARDBOARD-BOX CORNER

All that's needed to make enlargements from 8mm. movie film is an enlarger, some 4 by 5-in. cut film and a fine-grain developer. The procedure is much the same as when making any enlargement except that the movie-film positive is projected on regular film first to produce the negative from which the final print is made. The film for the negative should be a fine-grained panchromatic type.

First step, of course, is selection of the scenes from the movies that you wish to enlarge. Because the picture will be magnified many times, the frames should be those which are in sharpest focus. Place the film strip in the negative carrier of the enlarger so that at least five frames of the scene can be projected at the same time, and be sure to mask the strip carefully, Fig. 2. If the enlarger has a glassless carrier, place one edge of the strip so that its entire length is held between the carrier plates to prevent possible buckling. Then, as before, mask off the rest of the opening. Let the loose ends of the film hang down out of the way, Fig. 1.

In the darkroom, cut the 4 by 5-in. film lengthwise so there are two strips, each 2 by 5 in. If a cardboard-box corner is used to position the film on the trimmer, Fig. 3,

the task will be much easier and the results will be accurate. To project the movie film, place the carrier in the enlarger and focus on the easel so that each frame is about 1 in. wide. Then place the cut film on the easel and project the 8mm. frames on it. Five frames should about cover the length of the strip.

With five frames on the same film, it's possible to give each one a different exposure, much in the same way that a test strip is made on enlarging paper. At first it will be necessary to do a little experimenting; for example, try exposures of 1 sec., 2 sec., 4 sec., 8 sec. and 16 sec. with the lens set at f:11. However, the exposure will depend somewhat upon the light source in the enlarger and the speed of the film being exposed. Once the approximate exposure range necessary for the materials and equipment you have has been determined, the 5-test strip should cover scenes from most films.

The negatives that are made will be about the same size as 35mm. film. As mentioned, use fine-grain developer and avoid too much contrast. Then select the best frame and enlarge it as you would any other negative, using a matte-finish or similar paper to avoid grain.

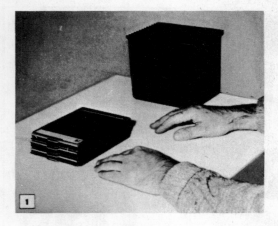

HOW TO PROCESS SHEET FILM

For the advanced amateur photographer considering purchase of a professional-type "press" camera, here is a method of processing sheet film that will help to produce good negatives

Fig. 1. Before unloading exposed film, organize work area in darkroom. Stack film holders at center of table, place film hangers on pegs with retainers flipped open, be sure developing solution is at 68 deg. F.

Fig. 2. Before turning off lights, turn locking pins on holders to center position so slides can be readily withdrawn in dark. Room must be totally dark from now until film is removed from hypo

Fig. 3. When removing film, anchor holder to table by pressing along bottom edge with right hand. Draw out slide about 2 in. with left hand and remove film, being careful not to touch emulsion with fingers

Fig. 4. Hold film hanger upright with left hand, slide film into channels and close loading flap. If film doesn't fit loosely in guide channels, open flap and remove and reinsert film properly

Fig. 5. Place loaded film hanger in empty tank. Repeat with successive hangers, using hand as spacer to prevent scratching film. Later, transfer entire group to developing tank at once. If fast-acting developer (3 to 5 min.) is used, stay with films until timer rings, immerse them in water 2 min., hardener-hypo bath 10 min., and water wash 30 min.

Fig. 6. Daylight tank permits processing sheet film outside of darkroom. After loading grooved reel with exposed film in total darkness, place reel in tank, secure lid, fill with developer and agitate with rod

Fig. 7. Before loading film, insert slides ½ in. into holder. In darkroom open bottom flap and slide film in guides with notches in upper-right corner, emulsion side up. Fig. 8, after film is inserted, press end flap down and push slide in until flap is engaged. Then turn locking pin to closed position to prevent slide from being pulled out of flap accidentally

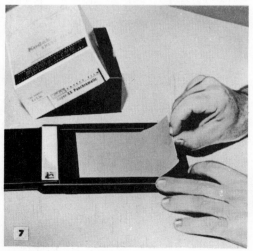

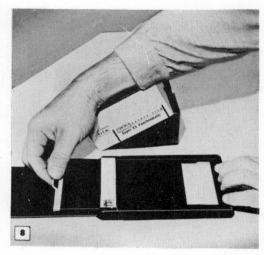

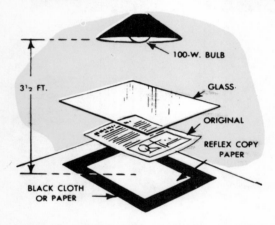

Note that copy at left is more contrasty than original at right. Lines and details are much sharper

COPYING
WITHOUT
A CAMERA

By Rolfe F. Schell

REFLEX paper makes it possible for anyone to copy an illustration, diagram or other drawing photographically without a camera, and directly from a book or magazine without mutilating the printed page. It can be done in a darkened kitchen or bathroom, and the chances are you already have the few items of equipment necessary.

Reflex copy paper is a sensitized paper which can be exposed only when the light source comes from the emulsion side. Light directed through the paper from the back side has no effect upon the emulsion. Only when the light reflects from the white of the prototype and back to the emulsion is the paper exposed. Reflex copy paper is available from photo and office-supply stores in sheets 8 x 10½-in. size and costs but a few cents per sheet. It must be handled in total darkness except during development which can be done in subdued yellow-green light.

As for equipment, you will need a piece of black paper or cloth, a sheet of clear glass, a 100-watt bulb and glass baking dishes to serve as developing trays. The

100-W. BULB

GLASS

3½ FT.

ORIGINAL

REFLEX COPY PAPER

BLACK CLOTH OR PAPER

When original has printing on both sides, back the copy paper with black cloth to prevent double image

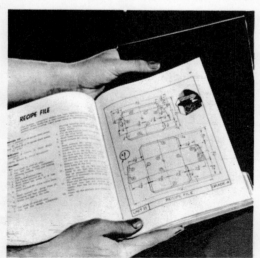

Develop until impression comes out boldly. If no impression shows after 30-60 sec., lengthen exposure

black paper or cloth is used when the original has printing on two sides. Placed underneath, the black backing prevents the light from reflecting back to the sensitized paper and picking up unwanted printing on the reverse side. The glass is placed over the original to keep it and the reflex paper in close contact so that sharp reproductions will result. The bulb should be suspended about 3½ ft. above the work and the paper exposed for six to eight seconds. The reflex paper becomes a paper negative when developed, from which regular positive prints can be made. To reproduce copy with printing on one side only, such as a letter, remember that the paper reflex is placed emulsion side up. To reproduce copy with printing on both sides, such as the page in a book, the reflex paper is placed on the copy, emulsion side down. ★ ★ ★

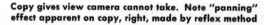

When copying from curved surface such as a label, rotate can slowly to assure uniform exposure

Copy gives view camera cannot take. Note "panning" effect apparent on copy, right, made by reflex method

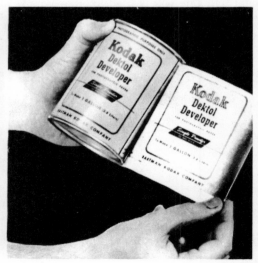

To make contact prints from wet negatives, wet enlarging paper is placed on ferrotype plate, after which negative strips are placed on top of paper, emulsion to emulsion, and exposed with the enlarger light

QUICK CONTACTS FROM WET NEGATIVES

For the photography hobbyist who wants contact prints in a hurry, here is an easy way of producing them without having to wait until processed negatives are dry. An enlarger and a ferrotype plate are the only pieces of darkroom equipment needed to do this. Begin by immersing an unexposed sheet of 8 x 10-in. enlarging paper in water for a few minutes. Then, allow it to drain while cutting the film into strips of four frames. Place the paper, emulsion side up, on the ferrotype plate and arrange the negative strips on top, emulsion side down. Wipe lightly with a damp sponge to flatten the negatives. Then expose the paper in the same manner as when using a contact printer. After exposure, immerse the negatives and paper in water to separate them, as the emulsion surfaces tend to adhere to each other.—G. Robert Smith

Bandage boxes of the type shown make handy pocket-size carrying cases for 35-mm. film cartridges when they are removed from their containers and wrapped in metal foil. One box is used for unexposed film, one for exposed. — Walter E. Burton

Solutions for film processing can be warmed to the correct temperatures quickly and easily by beaming a 100 to 200-watt light bulb on the solution in a graduate. Use a gooseneck desk lamp or photo flood reflector to concentrate the heat.

In the darkroom you spend considerable time working either in total darkness or in very subdued light. Likely you know the place as well as you know the inside of your pocket but unless there is adequate storage space you may discover at a critical moment that some needed item has been mislaid. Groping for it in the dark may give you ideas about how things should be arranged. Here are good, practical suggestions that will help

PLANNING THE DARKROOM

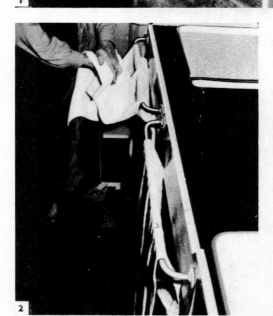

INVESTMENT ALONE won't make a darkroom easy to work in, but a carefully planned darkroom, even one very modestly outfitted, will enable you to save time as well as money. Also a darkroom well planned may enable you to improve the quality of your work. For example, vibration caused by a machine in the building may be fogging enlarged prints. If the darkroom is in your home, the motor of an electric refrigerator or automatic heating plant might transmit enough vibration through a floor to your enlarger to cause this trouble. Traffic on a busy street also could set up a vibration that would affect an enlarger. To prevent this, place thick pieces of sponge rubber under either the enlarger or the feet of the table on which it sets. A simple layout with all materials and equipment conveniently at hand is best. Figs. 1 to 4 inclusive are good examples.

Most photographers—amateurs and professionals alike—are inventive and resourceful. Their ideas on darkroom time-

Keep extra trays on shelves under the sink board. With this arrangement it won't be necessary to stack them one on top of the other. If you turn each one upside down it will always be dry and free from dust

Reaching for a metal pull chain on an outlet-box switch with wet hands isn't accepted practice in the safe, workable darkroom. Attach cords to switches and let them swing above your head within easy arm's reach

savers are worth studying closely. In a few darkrooms you will see a complicated system of light switches. Some of these may be located where wet hands must grope near an electrical outlet box or reach high for a metal pull chain. Not so good, in fact, this arrangement could be dangerous under certain conditions—maybe a wet floor or faulty wiring. A better, handier and safer arrangement is shown in Fig. 4 where the lights are operated by cords attached to the switch and to the wall so that they swing at an easy-to-reach height above the operator's head. In the course of average work in the darkroom, you will often find it necessary to turn on a white light. Unless this light is shielded effectively you'll be momentarily blinded. Not only inconvenient and uncomfortable, but a serious strain on the eyes if continued for any length of time. It's a simple matter to rig shades over or around the lighting fixtures so that light will be directed upon the work.

When processing prints, it's annoying to have to fumble under the sink for the necessary trays. Build a rack for them under the sink board where they can lie upside down, Fig. 3. That way they'll stay dry and they won't get dusty. Wastebaskets that permit discarded wet prints to drip puddles on the floor are troublemakers. A basket too small to hold an evening's quota of discards is a time waster. Get one that's big enough and make sure it's watertight. Install it under the drainboard where it's always handy.

If your darkroom "puts its mark" on your clothing, it is possible you can save expense by fastening buffers around the sink and drainboard. Measure the edges and buy towel racks, or make them of ¾-in. dowels. Fasten to the business edge of the sink and drainboard where they will protect your clothing as you lean over the work. To further protect your clothes and to add a handy accessory, hang thick towels over the buffers by thumbtacking one end of each towel to the lower edge of the board and draping the towel over the buffer as in Fig. 2. Run a splash bead or rail around the edge of the drippy area, to prevent chemicals from slopping over onto

the floor. Rubber aprons are clothes-savers, too. You'll see them in many a good darkroom. The money they save in clothing and cleaning bills can be invested toward a new print trimmer or maybe a box of matte paper.

If your darkroom has a concrete floor, you can cushion your feet by wearing wool socks and thick-soled shoes. Or better, do a little light carpentry. Nail 2-in. strips on crosspieces, with ½-in. spaces between strips, to form a springy floorwalk. There's a lot of footwork in the darkroom and a little attention to comfort at floor level pays real dividends.

Many a darkroom boasts an imposing collection of thermometers, but often lacks the one that it should have. That's the one hanging on the wall near the developing tray. Air temperature acts on open trays of developer, regardless of how many heaters or chillers you may have. With a thermometer

5—Frames screened with galvanized wire and built into the space under a table provide a convenient means of drying matte prints between blotters

6—To prop the wash tray at a more convenient height use glass jars with screw tops. Level the tray by turning the screw caps up or down

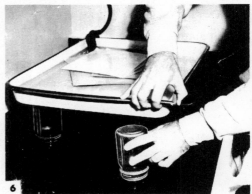

7—A windshield wiper is just the thing for squeegeeing wet prints. Treated in this way, prints will dry between the blotters in less than half the time

8—This hinged shelf supports a ferrotype tin while prints are being placed on it from the wash water. The drippings naturally run into the sink

9—An addition to the drainboard folds back against the wall when it's not needed. This makes extra floor space available for any other work

10—Plug-in outlets are a convenience, and thought must be given to the location of each one. All wiring should be installed in thin-walled conduit

11—Correct temperature for developer is important. If darkroom temperature varies, use a baby-bottle warmer. It warms the solution in a jiffy

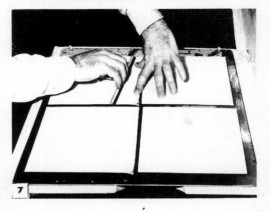

telling you what's happening to the air temperature, it's easier to keep watch on temperatures of the stop-bath and hypo.

Those hard-working blotters deserve a place all their own. Frames screened with galvanized wire, built into the space under a table or wide shelf, provide means of drying matte prints between blotters or under blotters, Fig. 5. Then too, you can sandwich ferrotype tins between them to save the tins from accidental scratching.

Raising the wash tray a few inches above sink-board level for protection against splashing is simply and quickly accomplished by placing three or four glass jars under the tray. To level a tray on a sloping surface, put screw-top jars under it and adjust the tops until water level in the tray looks right, Fig. 6.

For speeding up the drying time of prints, give them a squeegeeing with a windshield-wiper blade before rolling the prints under blotters. You'll save wear and tear on the blotters and you'll keep the floor drier. Do the squeegeeing on a ferrotype tin, Fig. 7.

Slapping wet prints on ferrotype tins always has been a swampy part of photography. You can eliminate much of the dripping by building a hinged drainboard to hold the tin while you're putting the prints on it, Fig. 8. Let it drain into the sink. A half-moon shape cut from the upper end of the board will give you a place to take hold of the slippery tin. Two screws near the lower edge will prevent the tin from sliding into the sink. Hinge the board to the wall and provide a hook or cleat to hold it up out of the way, Fig. 9.

One of the stand-by items in the average darkroom is the rubber roller for rolling wet prints under blotters. A useful, indispensable tool, but it's always in the way unless a special place is provided for it. If you build a rack especially for the roller, where it will be at hand when needed, you add workability to one more phase of darkroom routine. Electrical gadgets are used frequently and they're great time-and-trouble savers. But if you have to rig up double or triple sockets and yards of extension cord, your darkroom will have the appearance of an ill-concealed booby trap. A few extra outlets in the electrical circuit will solve the problem. Because you'll be handling the electrical equipment with wet hands, foolproof wiring is essential, Fig. 10. See that those extra outlets are properly wired and insulated. To warm the developer, try an electric baby-bottle warmer, the kind that you immerse, Fig. 11.

It's only when you have the darkroom

Left, shelves near the enlarger are handy for printing paper. Incidentally, build a platform like this to raise your enlarging easel to a convenient height It saves a lot of squint and stoop. Above, darkroom should have housed shelf compartments. They take more time to build, of course, but you've got to "live" with the furnishings a long time, so have them handy

open or the white lights on that a good paint job on the walls, ceiling and fittings shows up. But paint regularly applied helps keep the place clean. Use flat black on surfaces where you don't want glare. Walls and ceiling can be most any color desired. It's best to use a semiflat paint rather than a high-gloss finish. Keep the painting material handy in a cabinet like that in Fig. 14.

A considerable portion of your work in the darkroom is spent in focusing the enlarging camera. Unless the easel is placed at a convenient height, you have to bend your back and twist your neck. This kind of thing isn't permissible in the smooth-working darkroom. Take time to build a platform to raise the easel waist-high Leave the front open, and use the former table-top as a handy shelf, Fig. 1. If your enlarger is extremely high and cramped by a low ceiling, maybe a hole can be cut in the ceiling and boxed in to admit the lamp house.

Because they are of top-heavy construction, enlargers have a tendency to wobble. A wobbly enlarger wastes time and good printing paper. Vibration can be avoided by applying sturdy braces of flat iron to the top of the enlarger column. Two extra feet will provide a wobbleproof stance. Fasten the braces to the wall or ceiling, where they will be out of the way.

Spare corners are good spots for shelves, Figs. 12 and 13. The average darkroom has sufficient space but often the furnishings are not arranged to make the most of the space available. Shelves help. Big ones or little, they are needed for storing supplies where they won't clutter up the floor. They simplify the filing problem. If you want real efficiency and have the space, build a darkroom annex to be used as a film room. It's a smaller version of the main darkroom, but limited to the loading and processing of films. It will permit two-man operation and will give your films a higher degree of protection from light, dust and chemicals. In this film annex, you can build a lot of workability into a small space. A hinged shelf will make a film-loading table,

Paper cutter is located in recessed cabinet at right end of sink. Ferrotype storage racks are below sink

View of the right side of the darkroom through the sliding door shows neat appearance of flush cabinets

"Dream" Darkroom Takes Little Space

By William G. Waggoner

AFTER YEARS of using makeshift dark-rooms in kitchens or bathrooms, I finally built a "dream" darkroom, in which were incorporated ideas worked out during the many frustrating hours spent with my improvised setups. A portion of a garage, an area measuring 8 x 10 ft., was used for the darkrooms, although any small area could be remodeled in a similar manner. Because nothing projects from the walls except the enlarger, a minimum amount

Typewriter was included in equipment in original darkroom, stationery is stored in cabinet above it

of floor space is required for the dark room.

First step in construction is to build false walls 10 in. out from the original back and side walls. In this 10-in. space are located all the cabinets for storing equipment and supplies. Dimensions for all cabinets must be determined before the false-wall framing is erected, as the wall studs must be spaced to accommodate the widths of the various cabinets. All cabinets are built as indicated in the lower left-hand detail on the facing page, each one being simply a box assembled with glue and screws and screwed to the wall studs. The front edges of each cabinet project beyond the face of the studs the thickness of the material to be used as a wall covering. When the covering is applied, the cabinets will be flush with the surface. Dimensions shown on the cabinet in the detail are for one make of standard typewriter. Each cabinet must be dimensioned to accommo-date the material or piece of equipment it is to contain. Note in the detail that the desk lid of the cabinet, cut from ⅝ or ¾-in. plywood, is fitted with a piano-type hinge that is screwed to a cross piece attached just inside the front edges of the cabinet. The distance from the hinge center to the bottom of the cabinet is the same as the

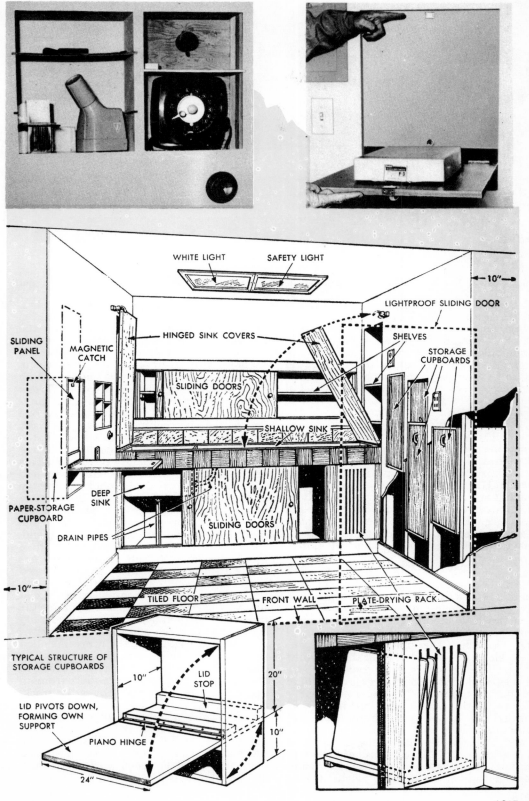

WHITE LIGHT SAFETY LIGHT

LIGHTPROOF SLIDING DOOR

SLIDING PANEL

MAGNETIC CATCH

HINGED SINK COVERS

SHELVES

STORAGE CUPBOARDS

SLIDING DOORS

SHALLOW SINK

10"

PAPER-STORAGE CUPBOARD

DEEP SINK

SLIDING DOORS

DRAIN PIPES

10"

TILED FLOOR FRONT WALL PLATE-DRYING RACK

TYPICAL STRUCTURE OF STORAGE CUPBOARDS

10"

LID STOP

20"

LID PIVOTS DOWN, FORMING OWN SUPPORT

PIANO HINGE

10"

24"

1617

Hinged covers drop down to make sink a worktable. Cabinets are back of sink, shelves are at each end

distance from the front edge of the cabinet to the inside surface of the cabinet back. Thus, when the door pivots on the hinge, the lower end of the door rests against the underside of a stop at the back of the cabinet. With this setup, the cabinet lid is self-supporting, requiring no external braces or legs to keep it in a horizontal position. When equipment is fastened to the inside surface of the doors, as is the typewriter in the lower left-hand photo, page 1616, weight of the equipment will keep the door in the closed position without need of any sort of latch. The paper-storage cabinet, upper right-hand photo, page 1617, differs from the other cabinets by having an inner, light-tight door. It slides in grooves cut in the sides of the cabinet and through a slot cut in the top. Because no equipment is attached to the door, a magnetic latch is used to hold it closed.

Spacesaving Features

Another spacesaving feature of the darkroom is a combination sink-worktable. Two hinged covers of ¾-in. plywood, covered with linoleum or plastic laminate, form the worktable that swings up out of the way when the sink is used. Screen-door closers are used to hold them against the walls. The sink was custom-made at a sheet-metal shop, and is painted with liquid rubber on the inside. It has a deep and a shallow basin. The deep basin has a perforated pipe coiled in the bottom through which water is run, causing tiny jets of water to keep the tank water agitated for thorough print washing. Depth of the water in both basins is controlled by standpipes that consist of lengths of plastic tubing

cemented in holes cut in sink stoppers. Water flowing in the shallow basin serves as a water-temperature control for the developer, stop bath and fixer chemicals that are in floating trays. Water from the shallow basin drains into the deep basin.

Cabinets under the sink have sliding doors that run on T-shaped tracks. Track of this type is available at most building-supply and some hardware stores. At one end of the sink cabinet is a storage rack for ferrotype plates, as indicated in the lower right-hand detail page 1617. Above the sink at the back and ends are shelves and cabinets for storage of equipment and supplies, as shown in the photo at the top of this page. Here again, the 10-in. space is used to good advantage. Sliding doors also are used on the cabinets back of the sink, open shelves are located at each end. Near the center of the left-hand wall of the darkroom is a shelf on which the enlarger is located. To its right are recessed shelves on which is kept material used with it. A timer is wired into an outlet box at the back of one shelf, which eliminates the need for any exterior wiring. The only cord showing is the one from the enlarger. A white light and a safelight are installed in boxes built flush with the ceiling. The door of the darkroom is a sheet of plywood that is suspended on nylon rollers from an overhead track. A cornice over the track, a recess at one side and at the bottom of the door, plus a felt strip along the other side, makes it light-tight. No recess is required for the full door, as it slides along the wall inside the darkroom. A hinged door also could be used, made light-tight and opening outward. ★ ★ ★

Dishpan Sink for Darkroom Beginner

What to use for a sink without spending a lot of money poses a problem for the amateur photographer interested in setting up a basement darkroom. The answer is a plastic dishpan. The plastic is soft and easy to cut, making it a simple job to cut a hole in the bottom for a standard bathtub-drain fitting. The flange around the edge of the pan permits it to rest neatly in an opening jigsawed in a plywood or hardboard counter covered with linoleum. In most cases, water can be piped to the darkroom by adding a line and faucet to the existing plumbing, and the sink can be drained with a length of 1½-in. plastic hose into a nearby floor drain. In the latter case, a trap isn't necessary on the sink fitting.

R. J. Phillips, Uncasville, Conn.

Filter on Faucet Assures Clean Water at Darkroom Tap

Clean water, free of rust flakes and other foreign particles, is important when it comes to processing film. Unfortunately, commercial filters are expensive and for this reason most amateurs use unfiltered tap water in the darkroom. However, an inexpensive and fairly simple water filter can be made as shown in the pull-apart drawing and attached directly to the sink faucet. Made entirely of brass, the body is a 3-in. section of kitchen-sink drainpipe which has a disk soldered at the bottom and a flange at the top. The bottom disk is drilled and tapped for a ¼-in. hose connection. The cover of the filter is held in place with eight capscrews turned into tapped holes in the flange. A gasket cut from an innertube goes between. A section of brass channel supports the filter screens and loosely packed cotton which filters the water.

Robert Michals, Freehold, N. J.

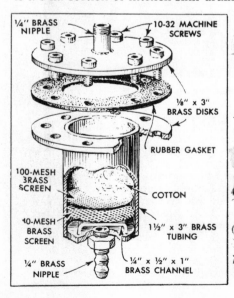

¼" BRASS NIPPLE — 10-32 MACHINE SCREWS — ⅛" x 3" BRASS DISKS — RUBBER GASKET — 100-MESH BRASS SCREEN — COTTON — 40-MESH BRASS SCREEN — 1½" x 3" BRASS TUBING — ¼" BRASS NIPPLE — ¼" x ½" x 1" BRASS CHANNEL

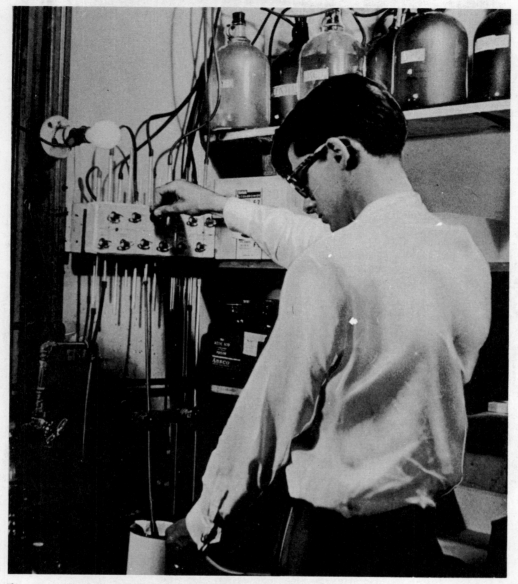

There are no bottles to handle in measuring out photo chemicals when they are kept on tap—just turn a cock

PHOTO CHEMICALS KEPT ON TAP

TURNING A VALVE to measure out photo solutions as you would a water faucet is a real darkroom convenience that will appeal to anyone who processes his photos at home. This is made possible with an easily installed vacuum-siphoning system which permits solutions to be tapped from stock bottles stored out of the way on an overhead shelf. The vacuum in the system is maintained by a device called an aspirator which is attached to the darkroom-sink faucet. Vacuum is created by running water through the aspirator. The vacuum also makes it possible to operate an efficient film agitator that is improvised from a windshield-wiper motor.

To install this system in your darkroom you'll need at least four 1-gal. bottles, seven glass stopcocks, four 2-hole corks to fit the bottles, five glass branch tubes, an aspirator and ¼-in. rubber and glass tubing. The glass stopcocks are the valves which control the flow of solutions kept on tap. All seven stopcocks are cast in a

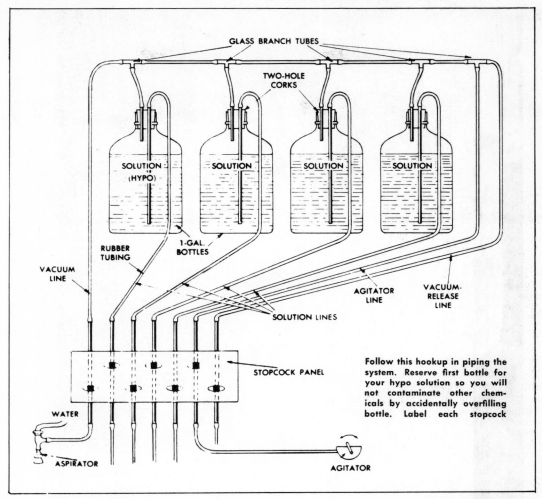

GLASS BRANCH TUBES

TWO-HOLE CORKS

SOLUTION (HYPO)

SOLUTION

SOLUTION

SOLUTION

1-GAL. BOTTLES

RUBBER TUBING

VACUUM LINE

AGITATOR LINE

VACUUM-RELEASE LINE

SOLUTION LINES

STOPCOCK PANEL

Follow this hookup in piping the system. Reserve first bottle for your hypo solution so you will not contaminate other chemicals by accidentally overfilling bottle. Label each stopcock

WATER

ASPIRATOR

AGITATOR

plaster-of-paris panel. A shallow cardboard box makes a good form for the casting as it can be easily stripped off. Holes are made in the sides of the cardboard box to insert the glass tubes attached to the stopcocks and the latter are positioned in the box in the manner shown in the drawing above. Pieces of wire and bits of metal mixed in with the plaster will reinforce the finished casting. Finally, each stopcock is labeled with the name of the solution it is to deliver, and the block is mounted at a convenient height on the darkroom wall.

Piping the System

The diagram above shows clearly how the stopcocks are connected with rubber tubing to the bottles, aspirator and agitator. You'll notice that each bottle cork is fitted with two lengths of glass tubing, one being long enough to nearly touch the bottom of the bottle.

Be careful in pushing the glass tubes through the holes in the corks. Wetting the corks with water will help make the tubes slide through easily, but you should **take the added precaution of wrapping the tube and cork with a towel to protect the hands in the event a tube should break.**

The vacuum of the system is controlled by the stopcocks at the ends of the panel, the one on the left being labeled vacuum and the one on the right, vacuum release. After each bottle is hooked into the vacuum line and connected to its respective stopcock in the manner shown in the diagram, the aspirator is connected to its stopcock and the agitator to its stopcock. The rubber tubing at the lower ends of the stopcocks should be long enough to reach into the darkroom sink.

The windshield-wiper motor is rigged up to rock a tray platform placed in the bottom of the darkroom sink. A bracket to hook it over the edge of the sink can be formed of coat-hanger wire and another piece of wire is used to connect the platform to the rocker arm of the motor. The platform can be either wood or metal, and a cork fastened to the underside at each end will provide pivots on which it can rock. To make the agitator work, turn on

Aspirator screws onto sink faucet and is connected to stopcock panel with length of rubber tubing

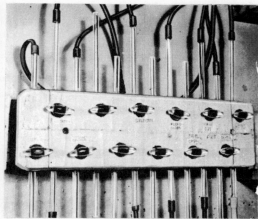

Stopcock panel controls flow of siphoned chemicals. Rubber tubing slips over ends of the glass tubes

the water faucet so water will run through the aspirator and open the stopcock labeled agitator. Adjust the flow of water through the aspirator so the agitator will rock the tray with a slow periodic movement. Avoid rapid agitation when developing film as this may cause flow lines on the surface.

Operating the System

To siphon solutions into the bottles, a vacuum must be created by running water through the aspirator. All stopcocks must be closed except the one which controls the bottle you are filling. As the vacuum increases, the solution will flow more rapidly into the bottle. Do not attempt to fill the bottle too close to the top or you run the risk of pulling the solution into the vacuum line and out through the aspirator. When the bottle is full, close the stopcock.

Don't let the container from which you are drawing the liquid become completely empty so as to draw air into the bottle. A column of solution must be left standing in the glass tube of each stopcock that delivers solution.

Let the first bottle of the group hold hypo. This will prevent any chance of the other solutions becoming contaminated should you accidentally overfill the hypo bottle. By keeping it first in line, any excess hypo will merely flow out through the aspirator. To insure cleanliness of the

Agitator is made from windshield-wiper motor and vacuum-operated by running water through aspirator

bottles after having exhausted the supply, draw some clean water into the bottle and drain it out again before refilling.

To tap the stock bottles, first open the vacuum-release stopcock and then the stopcock of the particular solution you wish to use. Should the tubing have no solution standing in it, turn on the water faucet and pull some water into the tube. Then release the vacuum again and the solution will flow. When not being used, seal off the system under a vacuum. This will help prevent oxidation of the chemicals that oxidate under normal air pressures. ★ ★ ★

Strong Hypo Substitutes for Rapid Fixing Solution

With the new single powder acid fix on the market it is possible for photographers to mix a double-strength hypo and get the same effect as a rapid fixing solution, and at less cost. The hypo mixture has none of the caustic properties of the ammonium-chloride rapid fix and has none of the corrosive effect of the latter. By using this double-strength hypo, films will clear equally as fast as when treated with a rapid

fix, and the hypo will actually last three to four times longer than a mixture of normal strength. When used on prints, the bleaching characteristics of a rapid fix are not present and the time allowance for immersion of the prints is not a controlling factor. A mixing ratio of acid fix, two parts to water, one part, is suitable for most general requirements.

LUMBERYARD PICTURE FRAMES

There are picture frames galore waiting for you at your lumberyard at a fraction of the price you would pay at a store. Stock builders' moldings offer a wide selection of shapes at pennies per foot

By E. R. Haan

6

WHO WOULD THINK of going to a lumberyard for picture-frame molding! But there you'll find an array of standard molding shapes that will frame your pictures for a song. Priced by the foot, the molding is nicely shaped from choice grades of pine and other woods and needs only to be mitered to length, Figs. 1 through 5. Some moldings are already rabbeted, on others the rabbet is formed with a second molding, Fig. 8. All have one thing in common, they're comparatively inexpensive.

Figuring Molding Lengths

To determine molding length required for a desired glass size, add the height and width of the glass and multiply by two. To this add the width of the frame multiplied by eight. For example, in case of an 11x14-in. glass-size, twice the height and width is 50 in. For a frame 2 in. wide, add 16 in. to 50, totaling 66 in. or 5½ ft. to allow for waste.

Unfinished molding to be given a transparent coating should receive a coat of sealer to avoid stains from glue. Many

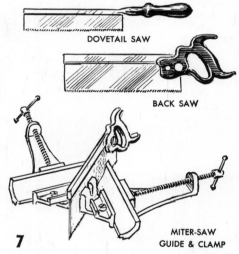

DOVETAIL SAW

BACK SAW

7

MITER-SAW GUIDE & CLAMP

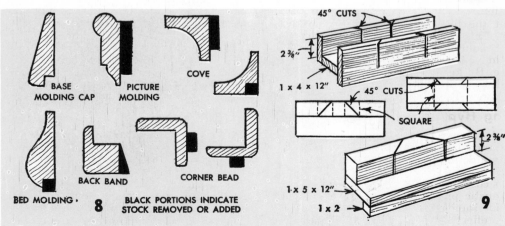

BASE MOLDING CAP

PICTURE MOLDING

COVE

BACK BAND

CORNER BEAD

BED MOLDING · **8** BLACK PORTIONS INDICATE STOCK REMOVED OR ADDED

45° CUTS

2 ⅜"

1 x 4 x 12"

45° CUTS

SQUARE

2 ⅜"

1 · x 5 x 12"

1 x 2

9

1 STOCK 1" LUMBER

2 FLUTED CASING

3 CROWN·MOLDING

4 SPRUNG COVE

5 DRIP CAP

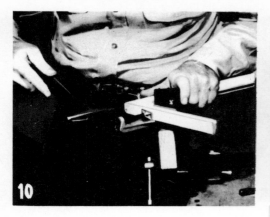

pleasing effects are obtained by making the grain of the wood contrast with a colored, semitransparent toner. Molding also can be covered with self-adhering sheet plastic having an imitation-wood finish.

Guides for Miter Sawing

If you haven't a circular saw to cut miters accurately, use a fine-toothed hand-saw such as a dovetail or back saw, Fig. 7, plus a suitable miter-sawing guide. Fig. 7 also shows an inexpensive combination miter-sawing guide and clamp.

A homemade miter guide and miter box are shown in Fig. 9. The dimensions given are intended for a back saw having a cutting depth of 2½ in. To mark a block or box for cutting the 45-deg. saw kerfs, use a sharp pencil to make perfect diagonal gauge lines as in Fig. 9. Also draw vertical lines on the sides for checking the cut while sawing. The 45-deg. kerfs in the guide should be made by the saw to be used in them or one of identical thickness and set. One edge of the kerf should be right on the fine diagonal lines.

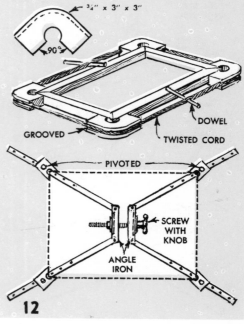

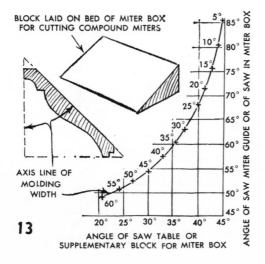

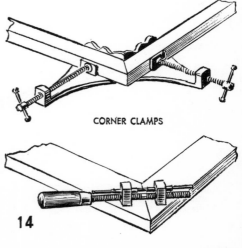

CORNER CLAMPS

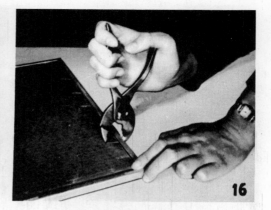

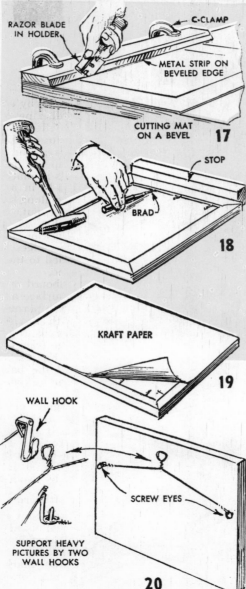

RAZOR BLADE IN HOLDER

C-CLAMP

METAL STRIP ON BEVELED EDGE

CUTTING MAT ON A BEVEL

17

STOP

BRAD

18

KRAFT PAPER

19

WALL HOOK

SCREW EYES

SUPPORT HEAVY PICTURES BY TWO WALL HOOKS

20

Using Miter-Saw Guides

Place the molding in the miter-saw guide or box so its back rests on the bottom and one edge comes snugly against one side. The molding must be held immovable—preferably clamped—in this position while sawing. Start the cut by drawing the saw backwards to prevent chipping the molding. To avoid a ragged back edge, place the molding on a strip of hardboard. If this is not done, the ragged edge must be removed carefully with fine sandpaper. Smoothly cut miters do not require sanding or planing, which sometimes changes the bevel or causes other damage.

Laying Out Frame for Cutting

For aligning the molding visibly, with the saw at the point where it is to cut, mark the outside edge of the molding. After cutting off one end at 45 deg., locate the mark for the next miter cut as follows: Measure the width of the molding from the outer edge to the bottom of the rabbet but not to the inner edge of the molding. Add twice this distance to the length of one edge of the glass, plus 1/16 in. for clearance. This gives the exact length of the molding along the outer edge from the corner already cut.

Compound Miters

Hopper-type frames require compound miter cuts. Lacking a circular saw with its accurate miter gauge and tilting arbor you can use a sloping block in a miter box, Fig. 13. When cutting compound miters, use a miter box that is adjustable. Extreme accuracy is highly important for sawing compound miters. For frames having sides that slope 45 deg., the miter-gauge or miter-saw angle is 54¾ deg., while the table tilt or the angle of the supplementary block in a miter box is 30 deg. You can find this in graph, Fig. 13, which covers various slopes of picture frames.

21

Assembling Frames

Check the four lengths of molding for accuracy. Assembling the pieces with glue and brads or finishing nails of suitable size is next. Often, small nails can be driven into soft molding without splitting it, even though no pilot holes are provided. But to forestall the risk of splitting, pilot holes are available, especially in hardwood. Generally a pilot hole needs to extend only from the outer edge of the molding to the miter cut—not into the joining molding.

After both pieces are glue-coated, place them together in a corner clamp, Figs. 10 and 14. Leave the molding in the clamps until the glue has dried.

Miter clamps that draw up the four corners of a mitered frame are shown in Fig. 12. However, when using these you glue the corners first but do the nailing after the glue has dried and the frame is removed from the clamp. For nailing, hold each side of the frame in a vise, using smooth, protective strips of hardboard on the finish side.

You can also glue and nail all corners of a frame freehand. To join corners freehand, chuck one member in a vise, using a protective pad against the molded surface and a backing piece such as plywood, Fig. 11. When joining molding, wipe off all excess glue with a damp cloth.

Mounting the Picture

Most pictures look best when offset by mats. Almost any thick paper of dull finish, preferably textured, will do. Thin paper is apt to buckle from moisture absorption. Best material to use is regular mat board. Interesting wood-grain and marble-ized effects on mats are possible by covering cardboard with self-adhering sheet plastic. Another attractive effect is obtained by using ⅛-in. perforated hardboard against a colored background.

The picture should overlap the mat no less than ⅜ in. Cut openings in matboard with a sharp razor blade held in a substantial holder; run the blade along a metal straightedge. For an angle cut, use a beveled straightedge as in Fig. 17. Mats often can be improved by black or colored ink lines drawn close to the edges as in Fig. 15. The picture is fastened to the mat with glue or removable tape.

The backing may be cardboard or corrugated board to bring the surface a trifle below the edge of the frame to permit the backing to be fastened with brads. On small frames you can push brads in gently with pliers, Fig. 16. For large frames, use a light hammer and punch, Fig. 18. After the brads are in place, seal the back of the picture with heavy paper to keep out dust, Fig. 19.

Screweyes used for hanging pictures generally are located from a third to a fourth of the picture height from the top edge as in Fig. 20. A loop formed at the center of picture wire as in Fig. 20 keeps a picture hanging straight, Fig. 6. Heavy pictures should be supported by two hooks.

Novelty Frames of Softboard

Attractive picture frames without glass, Fig. 21, can be made of soft wallboard. The outside edges are cut on a circular saw and then smoothed with sandpaper. The beveled cut is made as follows: Mark the position of the innermost edge on both

RABBET DEPTH IS
GLASS THICKNESS
PLUS 1/16"

1 x 2

3/8"

F.H. SCREWS

1/8" TEMPERED
HARDBOARD

1/8"

22

1 x 2

sides and cut halfway through the board from each side. Place the frame on blocks as in Fig. 21. With the finish side up, a medium-coarse file is used to dress off the beveled edges. Such frames are hung by gummed eyelet tabs as shown in Fig. 24.

Gang Frames

The frame in Fig. 22 holds several pictures of equal size and permits them to be exchanged quickly. Each picture is set behind a glass pane of the same size. Both are inserted into the upper rabbet and dropped into the shallow rabbet in the lower molding.

Imitation Frames of Sheet Plastic

Imitation wood frames can be made from strips of gummed sheet plastic. A backing of softboard gives the desired thickness, Fig. 23. Place the glass carefully on the two strips. Hold the glass, mat, and backing together firmly while turning the assembly over. Next, apply the two other strips to the glass. Before fastening these to the back, make a miter cut at each corner with a sharp razor blade to eliminate overlap, Fig. 25. To minimize opening mitered joints, avoid stretching the tape lengthwise when applying it. Pictures so assembled are provided with gummed eyelet tabs for hanging.

Besides the imitation wood tapes, many other colorful plastic tapes are available. When a decorating change is wanted, simply add a new tape to the frame. ★ ★ ★

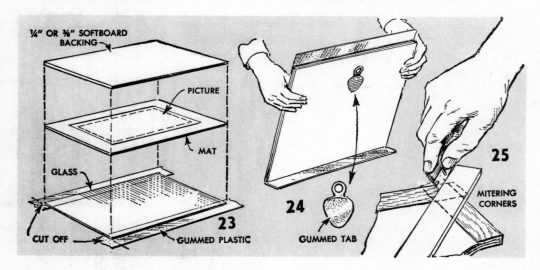

1/4" OR 3/8" SOFTBOARD BACKING

PICTURE

MAT

GLASS

CUT OFF

GUMMED PLASTIC

23

24

GUMMED TAB

25

MITERING CORNERS

MAKING AND REPAIRING BRIAR PIPES

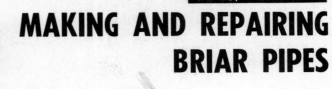

Pipecrafting calls for the craftsman's touch but anyone can make a good pipe with only a few tools—also repair that favorite old briar

GENUINE briar, as used in pipemaking, is a tough, hard rootwood and comes in pieces of comparatively small size. The grain in a single piece may vary from a distinct burl or "flame" figure through several gradations to a plain, flat grain. In cutting the rough blank for a pipe of conventional design from any but the choicest blocks of briar, the pipe maker often must modify the design to eliminate flaws in the material, or to take full advantage of the variations in the grain.

The bowl and shank of the conventional pipe are shaped from a

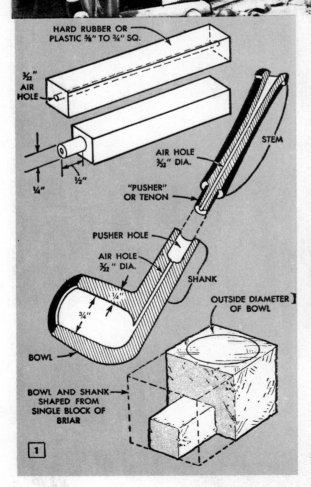

HARD RUBBER OR PLASTIC ⅝" TO ¾" SQ.

³⁄₃₂" AIR HOLE

¼"

½"

STEM

AIR HOLE ³⁄₃₂" DIA.

"PUSHER" OR TENON

PUSHER HOLE

AIR HOLE ³⁄₃₂" DIA.

SHANK

¼"

¾"

OUTSIDE DIAMETER OF BOWL

BOWL

BOWL AND SHANK SHAPED FROM SINGLE BLOCK OF BRIAR

1

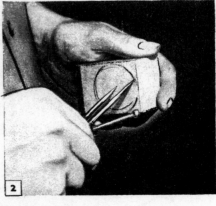

2

Scribe the inner and outer diameters of the bowl on the blank with sharp-pointed scriber

single blank of briar, Fig. 1, but the stem, or bit, usually is a separate part made from hard rubber or plastic. The bit is flattened at the outer end to form a comfortable mouthpiece. The air hole, usually $\frac{3}{32}$ in. in dia., is drilled lengthwise through the bit before the final shaping. Before cutting a blank of briar to the rough shape, examine it carefully for flaws and pattern of grain. Then square the top surface which is to be the top of the bowl. Scribe the inside and outside diameters of the bowl on the wood, Fig. 2. In sawing the blank to the rough shape, Fig. 3, make the first cut from the end of the shank to the bowl and the second down from the top of the bowl to meet the first cut. Allow waste for shaping the bowl and shank to exact size. Shape the shank roughly by running additional cuts in from the end of the shank to the bowl. Then two cuts run in from the outside to meet the last two at the shank will produce a blank shaped as shown in Fig. 4. Next, mount the blank in a special chuck in the lathe and bore the tobacco hole as in Fig. 5. Round the bottom of the hole to a uniform radius. Counterbore the shank while the work is still in the blank or make a special chuck to hold the semifinished part as in Figs. 7 and 8. Counterboring forms the air hole and the pusher hole as in Fig. 1.

Now the blank is ready for shaping, which is done on a recessed wooden disk faced with abrasive, Fig. 6. Both the outer face of the disk and the recessed center are coated with abrasive grains bonded to the surface with a special adhesive. In use, the speed of the abrasive disk should not exceed 2000 r.p.m., otherwise there is danger of burning and discoloring the work. The

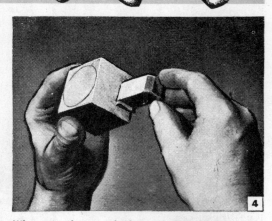

When sawed to rough shape, the completed shank-and-bowl blank is ready for sanding to final form

Boring the tobacco hole in the bowl, using a special chuck. Bottom of the hole is rounded uniformly

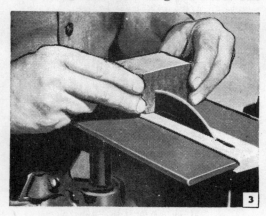

Next, the rough blank is sawed to shape with a circular saw. Be sure to allow stock for finish-sanding

Final shaping of bowl and shank is done on a recessed abrasive disk made especially for the purpose

After final shaping, the work is clamped in a specially made chuck tightened with a friction ring

Counterboring the shank to form the air hole and the pusher hole. Pusher hole must be of exact diameter

shaping procedure is simply that of bringing the shank and the bowl gradually to the rounded contours by alternately rounding over the corners of both shank and bowl. By working in this manner, the bowl and shank can be brought accurately to uniform shape and size.

At this stage the stem should be shaped. This is done on the abrasive disk but special care is taken to avoid overheating. Some hand-finishing will be necessary after assembly of the pipe. Turning the tenon to fit the pusher hole in the shank is the tricky job, but with care it can be done in a special chuck mounted on the lathe faceplate. Make several trial fits as in Fig. 9. After the stem is fitted to the shank, press it into the shank and touch lightly to the abrasive disk, Fig. 11, to finish the joint flush. If the stem fits too loosely, expand the end by heating it and inserting a metal taper pin as in Fig. 10.

High-grade pipes of fine briar usually are oil-finished and polished by hand. To do this, mix fine pumice and sweet oil to a light paste and rub the bowl, shank and

stem to a high luster. That's all. The pores of the wood in a good pipe should never be sealed with varnish or lacquer.

Figs. 12 to 18 inclusive detail the methods of repairing common breaks in the stem and shank. If the stem tenon snaps off, leaving a portion in the shank, Fig. 12, just square the broken end and turn a new tenon on the stem. A second method is the use of an insert tenon as in Fig. 13. If the stem is short, this method often is the best. If, on the other hand, the shank breaks close to the stem, cut the shank as in Fig. 14 and drill a new pusher hole. Pipe repairers often add a metal band, Fig. 16, as a part of this repair. When the shank breaks close to the bowl, the repair problem is somewhat more involved. Then the repairman uses what he calls a bone screw, which is merely a coarsely threaded tenon or dowel made from bone and available from pipe suppliers. Broken ends of the shank are squared and joined as in Fig. 15. Use a waterproof glue and, as soon as the glue has dried thoroughly, refinish the shank and stem on the disk as in Fig. 11, to

The stem is held in the same chuck when turning the tenon. Always trial-check the fit in the pipe shank

If pusher fits too loosely, expand it by holding the bit over heat and inserting taper pin in the air hole

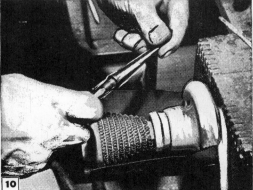

When the stem has been fitted to the shank, sand joint flush to assure a neat, close fit of these two parts

bring the parts of the joint flush. Then polish with oil and pumice. If care is taken in fitting the parts, the joint will be practically invisible. If the wood shows lighter at the joint (which it is likely to do on an old pipe) it can be brought back to the original color with a drop or two of stain. This is applied after finishing on the disk. Curved-stem pipes, Fig. 17, can be repaired in much the same way as a straight-stem pipe, provided the break is not too close to the bowl. In the former, the pusher hole must be taper-reamed. If the bit of a straight-stem pipe becomes unduly loose in the shank, the bit tenon is turned down slightly and fitted with a cork sleeve as in Fig. 17. The sleeves are available from dealers in pipes and accessories. Be careful when knocking out the ash to avoid striking the pipe against a hard surface. This may break the shank close to the bowl.

Keep pipes in a rack when not in use. As a rule, the type of rack which holds the pipe with the bowl down is considered best, although there is some difference of opinion among pipe smokers on this point.

If you break the shank of your favorite briar, it can be repaired by using a coarse-threaded bone screw

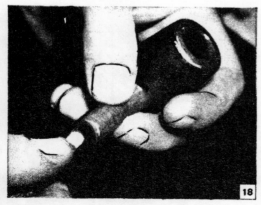

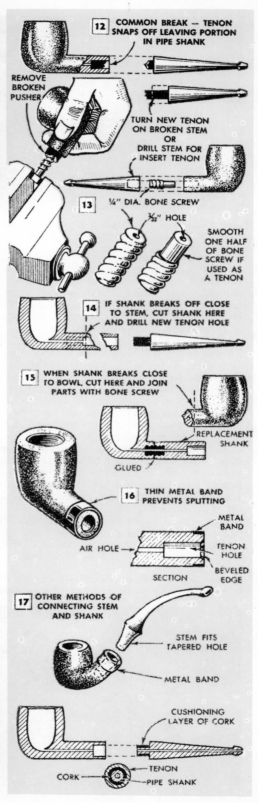

12 COMMON BREAK -- TENON SNAPS OFF LEAVING PORTION IN PIPE SHANK

REMOVE BROKEN PUSHER

TURN NEW TENON ON BROKEN STEM OR DRILL STEM FOR INSERT TENON

13 ¼" DIA. BONE SCREW

³⁄₃₂" HOLE

SMOOTH ONE HALF OF BONE SCREW IF USED AS A TENON

14 IF SHANK BREAKS OFF CLOSE TO STEM, CUT SHANK HERE AND DRILL NEW TENON HOLE

15 WHEN SHANK BREAKS CLOSE TO BOWL, CUT HERE AND JOIN PARTS WITH BONE SCREW

REPLACEMENT SHANK

GLUED

16 THIN METAL BAND PREVENTS SPLITTING

METAL BAND

TENON HOLE

AIR HOLE

BEVELED EDGE

SECTION

17 OTHER METHODS OF CONNECTING STEM AND SHANK

STEM FITS TAPERED HOLE

METAL BAND

CUSHIONING LAYER OF CORK

CORK

TENON

PIPE SHANK

An Occasional Piece for Colonial Furnishings

STORAGE PLANTER

By John Bergen

USED AS A ROOM DIVIDER or merely placed against a wall, this attractive planter serves a dual purpose. Its greenery adds a charming touch to a colonial setting and its base provides a roomy storage compartment that can be put to good use in every home.

Where a low planter is preferred, the piece can be made without the trellis. You have a choice of several appropriate woods, namely, knotty pine, redwood and cypress. The material list below gives the sizes and number of pieces needed, all of which are stock lumber, and the pull-apart drawing on the following page shows clearly how the whole affair goes together.

Since the back will show when the planter is used as a room divider, construction details will vary somewhat in adding ¾-in. paneling all around. Also, all four corners of the base should be mitered and both front and back rails scrollsawed. Otherwise, construction remains unchanged. Start with the base. Notice in section details E

MATERIAL LIST
(KNOTTY PINE, REDWOOD OR CYPRESS)

BASE
2 pcs.—2 x 4 x 16 in.—Rim side rails
1 pc.—2 x 4 x 30 in.—Rim front rail
1 pc.—2 x 4 x 22¾ in.—Rim back rail
6 pcs.—1 x 6 x 24¾ in.—Side members
6 pcs.—1 x 6 x 19 in.—Door members
1 pc.—1 x 2 x 108 in.—Cleat material
1 pc.—¾ x 2¾ x 108 in.—Cleat material
1 pc.—¾ x 3½ x 28⅛ in.—Back base
1 pc.—¾ x 3⅝ x 30 in.—Front base
2 pcs.—¾ x 3⅝ x 16 in.—Side bases
1 pc.—½ x 14 x 27 in.—Shelf (fir plywood)

1 pc.—½ x 15-3/16 x 28⅞ in.—Bottom
1 pc.—¼ x 27¾ x 25¼ in.—Back (hardboard)
4 flush-type colonial hinges
2 1¼-in.-dia. colonial knobs
2 ⅜-in.-dia. bullet catches with strikes
1 pc.—sheet metal 22 x 36 in.—Plant trough

TRELLIS
2 pcs.—1 x 4 x 36 in.—Ends
2 pcs.—1 x 4 x 24⅞ in.—Top and bottom
2 pcs.—1 x 4 x 17½ in.—Shelves
4 dowels—1-in.-dia. x 36 in. long

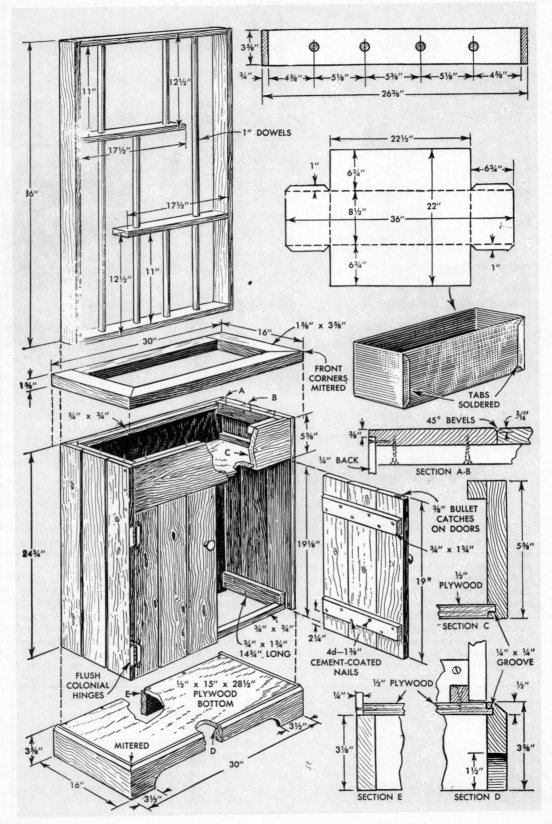

11"

12½"

1" DOWELS

17½"

17½"

36"

12½"

11"

30"

16"

1⅝" x 3⅝"

1⅝"

¾" x ¾"

A
B

C

5⅝"

¼" BACK

24¾"

FLUSH
COLONIAL
HINGES

E

¾" x ¾"
¾" x 1¾"
14¾" LONG

½" x 15" x 28½"
PLYWOOD
BOTTOM

MITERED

3⅝"

30"

16"

3½"

3½"

D

3⅝"

3½"

4d—1⅜"
CEMENT-COATED
NAILS

19⅛"

19"

2¼"

3⅛"

½" PLYWOOD

¼"

SECTION E

3⅛"

1½"

3⅝"

SECTION D

¼" x ¼"
GROOVE

½"

½"
PLYWOOD

SECTION C

5⅝"

¾" x 1¾"

⅜" BULLET
CATCHES
ON DOORS

45° BEVELS

³⁄₁₆"

⅜"

SECTION A-B

FRONT
CORNERS
MITERED

TABS
SOLDERED

3⅝"

¾"
4⅝"
5⅛"
5⅜"
5⅛"
4⅝"
26⅜"

22½"

1"
6¾"
6¾"

6¾"
8½"
22
36"

6¾"

1"

and D that the plywood used for the top is fitted flush with the top edges of the side rails. Three edges are rabbeted to fit grooves in the inner faces of the rails, while the back edge is left square for nailing into the 3⅛-in. back rail. This forms a rabbet along the rear edge to house the ¼-in. back panel. The chamfered edge around the three sides of the base can be planed after assembly.

The pieces that make up the ends of the storage compartment are made into 15¼-in. panels by screwing them to cleats placed at top and bottom. The cleats are made 1 in. shorter than the width of the built-up ends to allow for the thickness of the back and the doors. Note in section detail A-B that a rabbet is cut along the rear edge of each end

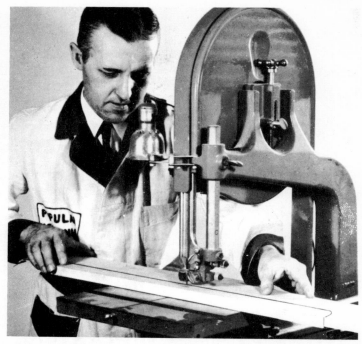

Toe-hole cutout in base apron is quickly cut with bandsaw. Both front and back aprons should be similarly cut when planter is room divider

panel and that a V-joint is formed between the individual boards by prechamfering the meeting edges slightly.

The trough compartment is formed by gluing and nailing the built-up ends to an L-shape assembly made up of a front board and a bottom board, joined in the manner shown in detail C. A ¾-in.-sq. cleat at each end provides support for the bottom board. Similar cleats along the front and back at the top take the screws that anchor the rim. The latter is made as a separate frame from 2 x 4 material. If the planter is to be used as a room divider, all four corners of the rim should be mitered to look best. Otherwise, the rear corners need only be butted. Dowels or splines at the mitered joints make the best construction, but an easier way is to simply glue and nail them and later conceal the nailheads with wood putty. The rim is placed flush at the back and centered so it overhangs ¾ in. at the sides and front. Glue it in place first and then drive the screws up through the cleats in predrilled holes. A short stubby screwdriver will do best here. As a room divider it might look better to let the rim overhang all around in which case the width of the rim frame should be increased to 16¾ in. The doors are made up in the same manner as the ends, chamfering the edges of random pieces to produce V-joints and gluing and screwing them to cleats placed across the back. If you don't care to make the sheet-metal liner yourself, take the pattern given to your local tin shop. If you make it yourself, buy a sheet of 22-gauge metal and cut it just like the pattern. By clamping a board 8½ in. wide and 36 in. long to the middle of the sheet metal, you can do a neat job of bending up the sides and tabs. You'll have no trouble in bending the ends inward. Notice that the tabs are on the outside.

The base is attached to the upper part of the planter by driving screws up through the plywood top and into the end cleats. Additional rigidity is gained in nailing the back panel in the rabbet at the back. A ¾-in.-sq. cleat is fitted across the front to provide a ledge strip for the doors. If you wish, shelves can be added to the storage compartment. In doing so, cleats should be first screwed to the ends to support the shelves. They can be left loose or glued.

The trellis section is a simple affair that is made from 1 x 4 material and 1-in. dowels. To assure perfectly aligned holes in the four cross pieces for the dowel uprights, stack the pieces in their respective positions, clamp, and drill through the four members at one time. By drilling through from the bottom, you can easily make blind holes in the members the dowels do not pass through. The dowels are locked in place by cross nailing, and the butted corners of the frame are merely glued and nailed. A couple of roundheaded screws will hold the trellis to the rim of the planter, flush with the back. ★ ★ ★

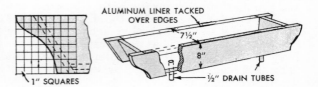

PLANTERS SET THE SCENE

ONE CAN USE outdoor planters to key the planning of nearly all outdoor-living areas. As an example, note how the replica above, Fig 1, not only is a decorative planter in itself, but also is, architecturally, a part of the house. Materials and finish have been selected to achieve this end. The covered well is made of used brick and is covered by a shale roof. Framing is of 3 x 3-in.

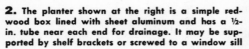

2. The planter shown at the right is a simple redwood box lined with sheet aluminum and has a ½-in. tube near each end for drainage. It may be supported by shelf brackets or screwed to a window sill

4. A simple shelf like this one may be decorated with a valance. The cedar "buckets" are cut, assembled with glue and then bound with aluminum bands

5. This planter is made of cypress which properly finished will well stand dampness and inclement weather. If made of pine, planters such as this should be lined with sheet metal or with tar

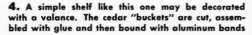

Flanking the entrance walk, planters such as this one add color and atmosphere to the house and grounds

redwood uprights secured with bolts and set below grade to a depth of about 1 ft. For strength, the unit is erected on a 4-in. concrete slab with the brickwork laid in after the uprights are installed.

The number of designs used to make outdoor planters is limited only by the imagination and resources available to the de-

signer. The size and shape of the lawn or garden area will, of course, largely determine the limits of what can be done. But once the practical possibilities have been assessed, imagination may be given free rein. If planters are used to divide an area, for example, the beginning of a geometrical motif is set, and a judicious use of smaller

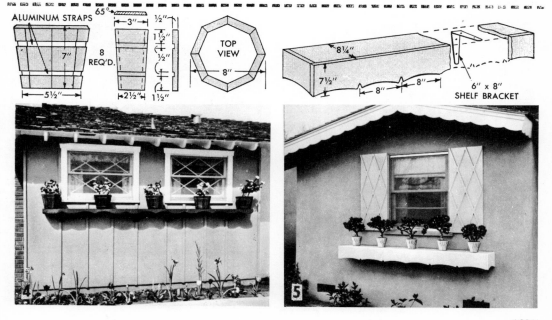

Cut flagstone has the advantage of being both pleasing to the eye and easy to manage in construction. This planter is made of layers of flagstone and has a grillwork of iron pipes supporting a wooden roof

Here, blocks of limestone were used to enclose a flower bed near the entrance of the house. Level with the surface of the porch, the planter becomes, in effect, an extension of the house itself

planters, flower beds and shrubbery, Figs. 7 and 9, may be used to further develop it. The use of wood and stone in a rather large planter may set the accent which the rest of the ground design repeats and develops. The use of plants also offers many possibilities. For instance, climbing vines and flowers in a central planter which has a trellis may be set midway between the house and the fence or walk. This may then be repeated in shallow planters bordering the area and by ivy climbing the house itself. Stone planters extending perpendicularly from the house midway into the lawn

area, as in Fig. 3. match the masonry construction of the house walls, which may again be repeated in stone-bordered flower beds flanking the house on two sides and along the front. The planter shown above is a good example of the rugged beauty of stone and of the use to which it can be put. It is made of cliff stones of various sizes and the spreading rock plants will eventually cover it. The contrast of leaf and stone will only serve to enhance its beauty. If desired. such planters may be made to extend the entire width of a lawn and thus serve as rustic stone fences. The

Wagon wheels add a picturesque quality to any lawn. This one was set in a shallow planter and is backed by a pedestal topped by a lamp. The planter is open at the bottom for drainage of the lush English ivy

Almost austere in its formality, this stone planter is set with a sword palm near the entrance of the house. Several of these placed on a concrete patio or veranda add an air of dignity to their surroundings

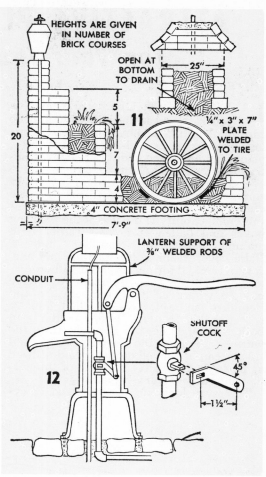

Homeowners in the dry Southwest will appreciate the decorative grace of these sand-filled cactus planters. They are made of cultivator disks welded to pipe flanges and set on pipes driven into the ground

planter in the photograph has a lamp and a bench running along one side.

Various objects, such as wagon wheels, or hand pumps, Figs. 8 and 11, serve to add a certain flavor to a garden's semiformal arrangement. This motif may be extended to replicas of the old oaken bucket set on window shelves, Figs. 2, 4 and 5, or to an open-"well" planter. For more sophisticated decoration, a patio may be decorated with individual "gardens," Fig. 10, or divided from the rest of the garden by brick planters with uprights extending to the patio roof as shown in Fig. 6. ★ ★ ★

Novel arrangement combines a means of watering plants and illuminating the lawn. A ½-in. pipe through the masonry has shutoff valve connected to the pump handle. Lamp is switched on from the house

A combination of concrete and colored pebbles forms the dish top of this striking patio planter

ATTRACTIVE PLANTING BOXES
for Your Indoor Garden
By C. W. Woodson

LIVING INDOOR GREENERY can be yours the year 'round with a little careful planning. And by using these planting boxes you can change room decor, plants can be moved about to create attractive color effects. As an example, a live evergreen can serve as a room divider in summer and as a living Christmas tree during the holiday season. The secret of this changeability is the use of the planting boxes and balled specimens rather than making permanent plantings indoors. Balled evergreens in the medium and narrow pyramidal forms, also many other low-growing shrubs, can be made to thrive indoors wherever light, temperature and humidity can be closely controlled. Usually it is possible to meet these conditions in both old and new homes. During the warmer months the larger plants and shrubs can be moved outdoors and utilized as portable decorative features of the permanent outdoor-garden plantings.

To assure long life, use redwood or cypress for planting boxes. Coat the interior with hot asphalt, or line with sheet copper, all joints being soldered. Drain holes in the bottom of the box are protected by extending short lengths of tubing through them, and soldering to the liner.

On these two pages are shown detailed drawings of a planting box that is suitable for a living Christmas tree. Stock for the sides is 1½-in. material, the bottom is 1-in. stock. The bottom is drawn by scribing a hexagon inside a circle. The radius of the circle is 6¾ in., which is within a fraction of an inch of being equal to the side of the inscribed hexagon. A slight adjustment of a compass will produce six equal divisions on the circle, to provide six sides for a hexagon. The stars for the planting box are cut from ¾-in. stock and are attached after the box is assembled with glue and screws. This particular container may be painted in bright colors in keeping with the holiday spirit, as it is used generally for a decorated Christmas tree.

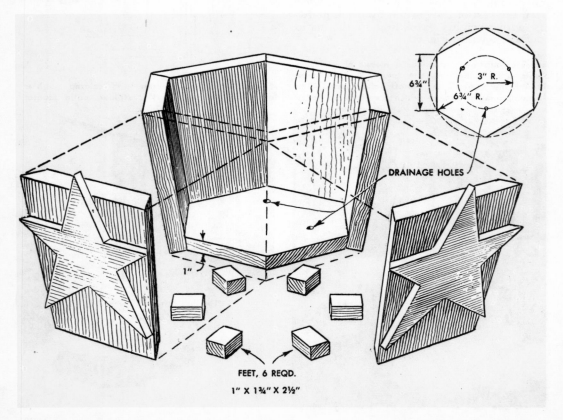

DRAINAGE HOLES

6¾"
6¾" R.
3" R.

1"

FEET, 6 REQD.
1" X 1¾" X 2½"

All plant boxes should be raised slightly by the addition of feet so air can circulate beneath and keep bottom dry. Also, all should have drainage holes bored in the bottom to allow excess water to escape. Pieces of broken pottery may be placed over the holes. Copper liners can be fitted to all boxes if you wish

9¾"

¾"

STAR

TOP VIEW, TUB PANEL

30°

1½"

8¾"

STAR, 6 REQD

10"

SIDE PANEL

BOTTOM

6¾"

7½"

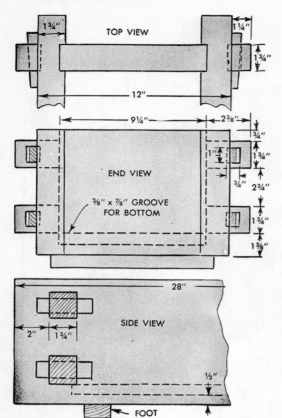

TOP VIEW

1¾" 1¼"

1¾"

12"

9¼" 2⅜" ¾"

END VIEW

1" 1¾"

¾" 2¾"

⅜" x ⅞" GROOVE
FOR BOTTOM

1¾"

1⅜"

28"

SIDE VIEW

2" 1¾"

½"

FOOT

On this page are shown the details of a rectangular planting box of more modern design. Despite its modernity, no nails or screws are used in its assembly. Instead, the ancient method of using wedge-shaped pegs is employed. A mortising bit and a drill press are handy in making the cutouts in the construction of this planting box, but a careful craftsman can use a regular wood bit and a wood chisel to obtain excellent fits between the various components. The sides of this box are cut from 1¾-in. stock, the bottom from ⅞-in. material.

Feet for this planting box are strips of wood. Some sort of feet or spacers are needed under all planting boxes that are portable, to allow for drainage and to assure circulation of air under a box. This will prevent any moisture that collects on the outside of the box from remaining long, and causing rot or mildew. A situation that might cause water to collect on the bottom of a planting box would be an overwatering which would cause water to run out the drain holes in the bottom of the box, and collect on the bottom. Such moisture might encourage the growth of harmful bacteria or fungi, that would produce a root-destroying disease in the soil.

On page 1643 is shown a square planting box that is ideal for small evergreens and ornamental shrubs. If you have ever

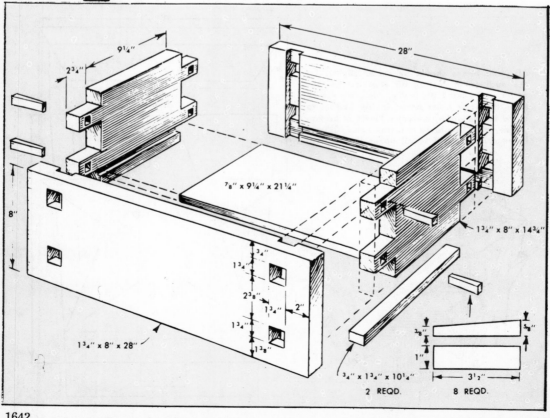

9¼"

2¾"

28"

⅞" x 9¼" x 21¼"

1¾" x 8" x 14¾"

8"

¾"

1¾"

2⅜"

1¾"

2"

1¾"

1⅜"

1¾" x 8" x 28"

¾" x 1¾" x 10¼"

2 REQD.

⅜"

1"

3½"

8 REQD.

wished you could occasionally change the character or appearance of your terrace by moving the planting to different locations, this container will permit you to satisfy that whim. Some plants that die out in the fall can be kept in bloom almost all year 'round if they are moved indoors before frost occurs. Planting boxes of varying sizes built in the same proportions and design as the one on this page will permit various kinds of shrubs and plants to be moved indoors to beautify your home during the long winter months.

Miniature rosebushes that bloom all year 'round, as well as dwarf fruit trees now are available, and would fit easily into any of the several planting boxes described in this article. Also, you might have a spot in your living room that would require a planting box of a special shape to fit properly. Build it in that space and bring summertime outdoor beauty into your home. It will be easier to forget the cold and blowing snow outside with green, blossoming shrubs inside your living room.

★ ★ ★

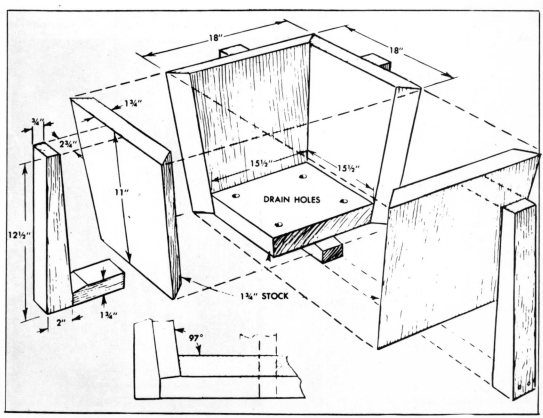

Skylights in ceiling provide adequate source of natural light for this garden planted beside a room divider

Bring Your Garden Indoors

PLANTS, whether big tropical varieties or small succulents, add a dramatic touch to the interior of any home. And modern building ideas make it easier to have an outdoor-size garden in your living room the year around. Skylights, for example, can provide enough sunlight to grow many kinds of plants along an inside wall or a room divider. And large windows near an outside door will sustain an attractive entryway garden.

In basementless homes an indoor garden can be built directly upon soil beneath the floor, as shown below

Indoor garden also can be located near the front door. The light source here is an entryway window

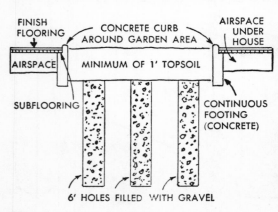

FINISH FLOORING

CONCRETE CURB AROUND GARDEN AREA

AIRSPACE UNDER HOUSE

AIRSPACE

MINIMUM OF 1' TOPSOIL

SUBFLOORING

CONTINUOUS FOOTING (CONCRETE)

6' HOLES FILLED WITH GRAVEL

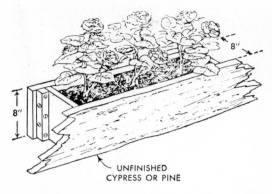

UNFINISHED
CYPRESS OR PINE

8"

8"

1

2

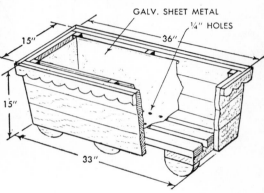

GALV. SHEET METAL

¼" HOLES

15"

36"

15"

33"

WINDOW BOXES

HANGING gardens placed at the window-sill level are of immense decorative value to both the interior and exterior of any home. Foliage and flowering plants, certain dwarf shrubs, evergreens, potted slips, succulents, and even trailing vines can be grown in a window-sill garden and they will thrive with a minimum of care. Some varieties grow best in full sunlight; others do well in partial shade, and some in full shade. This means that, by carefully selecting the plants, you can grow luxuriant hanging gardens on all four sides of the house in a single season. Groups of plants selected for a given location should have the same or similar soil preferences, and also similar temperature and sunlight requirements. Only low-growing plants with heavy stems and short foliage should be selected for second-floor window gardens, as these will be more directly exposed to high winds and beating rains. If shelves are used at the second-story windows, holes should be scrollsawed in the shelf boards so that the plant pots can be set in the holes to about half their depth.

This arrangement prevents the potted plants from being blown off the shelves. If soil is to be placed directly in the box, the latter should be made of wood with a removable metal lining of zinc or aluminum. Cypress is the most durable wood, with redwood and pine a second choice. The selection and preparation of soils are important. As the amount of soil is limited by the size of the box, the plant food of an ordinary soil will soon be depleted. A good mixture for window boxes is composed of dark garden loam, rotted leaf mold and sand in the proportions of 2 parts loam, 1 part leaf mold and 1 part sand. After these components are mixed, a complete fertilizer is added. Then the whole mass is mixed thoroughly and sifted through a ½-in.-mesh screen. To grow most varieties of succulents, proportions of the soil mixture should be 2 parts loam to 1 part coarse sand, no leaf mold being used.

In preparing the window box for planting, ½-in. drainage holes are drilled in the bottom in an over-all pattern measuring about 3 in. each way. Small pieces of

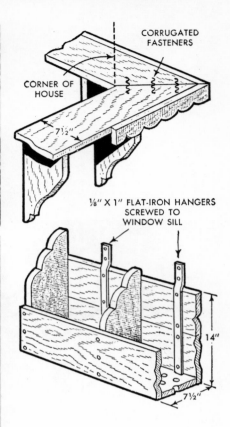

CORRUGATED FASTENERS

CORNER OF HOUSE

7½"

⅛" X 1" FLAT-IRON HANGERS SCREWED TO WINDOW SILL

14"

7½"

broken pottery (pieces from a flowerpot will do) are placed over each of the holes to keep fine material from sifting through. Then a 1-in. layer of coarse gravel, cinders or small pieces of broken pottery is placed in the bottom of the box. If the box is to be planted with succulents, the layer of this material should be 2 in. thick. Fill the box with the soil mixture to within about ½ in. of the top, pressing it down firmly. The mixture should be dry enough to handle easily without sticking to the fingers.

Plants to be grown in such a confined space as the average window box should be selected for type and habits of growth. Foliage plants with large individual leaves should not be planted adjacent to small, low-growing plants, except in extra-long boxes where the large plants can be placed at the ends of the box or in the center. If planted at random or alternately in a smaller box, the large leaves of the taller foliage plant will shade the smaller plants during some part of the day and may thus affect the rate and extent of growth. As a result of spreading root systems, large and vigorous growers also will rob small plants of needed soil fertility. Window-box gardeners generally select low-growing flowering plants for the sunny side, foliage

plants and trailing vines for the areas of partial and full shade and small evergreens for the year-round window garden. Suitable evergreens may be any of the low, spreading varieties which grow slowly. Certain plants that will not mature fully in the shorter growing seasons of the colder regions are suitable for outside plantings only in the warmer climates.

Most window-box plantings must be sprayed or dusted regularly to keep off insects and prevent disease. Spray solutions can be applied with a syringe, and prepared dusts with an applicator usually furnished with the product. As a rule, only annuals are planted in outside window boxes in temperate regions. In most cases, potted plants placed in or on window boxes or shelves are taken inside during the colder months. This simplifies the insect and disease-control problem, at least to some extent. Plantings of evergreens that are well established will flourish the year 'round in exposed locations if they are properly cared for during the summer and are thoroughly watered just before the coming of freezing temperatures. At this time, a thorough watering is especially important for if the soil freezes "dry" the plants are likely to die.

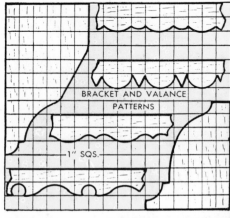

TOE-
NAILED

LAG
SCREW

⅛" X ¾" FLAT
IRON

BRACKET AND VALANCE
PATTERNS

1" SQS.

Window boxes and shelves pictured and detailed in Figs. 1 to 5 inclusive are designed for mounting outside the window. Those shown in Figs. 6, 7 and 8 are built as a part of the house and, in the warmer climates, can be used for plantings of perennials. Shelves are supported on bandsawed brackets and decorated with an edging or valance in a scrolled design as shown on the corner shelf in Fig. 3. Several scroll-sawed designs for brackets and edgings are shown in the crosshatched detail above. The shelf in Fig. 5 is supported by flat-iron scrolls which are especially attractive when used on walls of white siding or stucco. When shelves are attached to the wall with brackets, the inner edge should be set out from the wall about ¼ to ½ in. so that water and dirt do not collect at this point. Use brass screws for fastening the brackets to wooden walls and masonry drive nails or expanding fasteners on masonry walls. In either case, the fastenings should be sufficiently strong to support the weight of the box when it is full of damp soil.

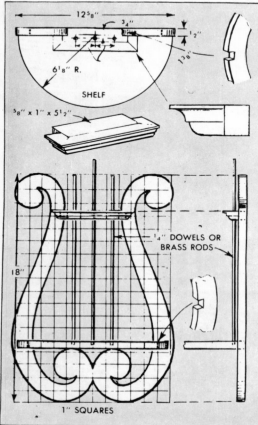

SHELF

12 5/8"

3/4"

1/2"

1 3/8"

6 1/8" R.

5/8" x 1" x 5 1/2"

18"

1/4" DOWELS OR BRASS RODS

1" SQUARES

FOUR WALL PLANTERS
for attractive display of your plants

POTTED PLANTS grown indoors always are more attractive and more easily tended when they have their own special racks or shelves. And whether your taste and decor run to colonial, modern, classic or conventional, you will find a style of shelf or rack described in this article that will meet your needs. As with any job, power tools will reduce both the time and labor required to make the plant holders, but hand tools are entirely adequate.

Classic Lyre

The classic lyre shape of the shelf detailed on this page can be jigsawed from a single piece of plywood or cut from two pieces of solid stock. In the latter case, one half of the pattern is drawn on one piece of stock, which is placed over another and both pieces are jigsawed at one time. A dowel glued and fitted in blind holes at the point where the side scrolls join will hold the lyre together at the lower end, and the decorative cross piece near the top will hold the upper ends of the lyre in position. Adding the shelf and the vertical members, which can be 1/4-in. dowels or brass rods, will give rigidity and strength to the

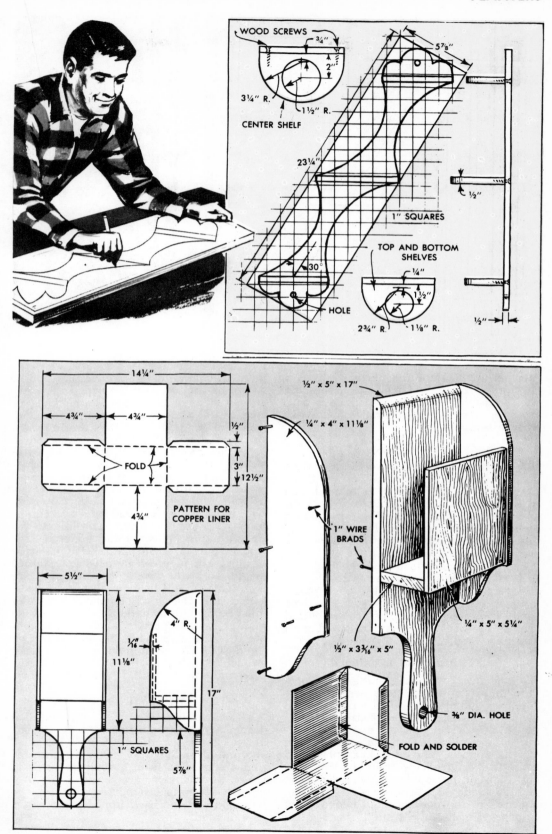

WOOD SCREWS

3/4"

2"

3 1/4" R.

1 1/2" R.

CENTER SHELF

5 7/8"

1/2"

23 1/4"

1" SQUARES

TOP AND BOTTOM SHELVES

1/4"

1 1/2"

30°

2 3/4" R.

1 1/8" R.

1/2"

HOLE

14 1/4"

4 3/4"

4 3/4"

1/2"

FOLD

3"

12 1/2"

4 3/4"

PATTERN FOR COPPER LINER

1/2" x 5" x 17"

1/4" x 4" x 11 1/8"

1" WIRE BRADS

1/4" x 5" x 5 1/4"

1/2" x 3 3/16" x 5"

5 1/2"

4" R.

1/16"

11 1/8"

17"

1" SQUARES

5 7/8"

3/8" DIA. HOLE

FOLD AND SOLDER

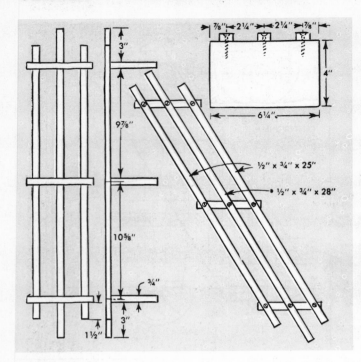

finished shelf. Note that inside edges of the lyre scrolls are notched to accept the shelf and top cross piece, which adds both strength and neater appearance to the finished assembly.

Modern Design

Modern design is featured in the next shelf, which actually consists of three brackets arranged in steps. A hole is bored in each shelf to accommodate flowerpots, as indicated. The top and bottom shelves have a 2¼-in.-dia. hole, the center shelf has a 3-in.-dia. hole, so that the larger pot is located on the center shelf.

Again either plywood or solid stock can be used. If solid stock is used, a 2-ft. length of ½ x 6 is adequate for the back piece. For greater strength, 1-in. stock could be used. The three bracket shelves are butted against the back piece and fastened with glue and wood screws.

Early American or Colonial

Maple furniture and shining brass provide the decor which goes best with the "flour scoop" planter, but it will look well even in a modern kitchen. Extremely simple in design, only a few curves are required and these are shown on a pattern of 1-in. squares. The curves can be varied from the original for individuality, and both sides of the paddle-shaped back of the planter made identical by first drawing one half of the pattern on a folded sheet of paper and cutting it out to form a full

pattern. The unfolded pattern then can be traced on the stock with a pencil. The two curved sides of the scoop are clamped or nailed together temporarily and jigsawed at one time, to assure that they are the same size and shape. The scoop is designed to have flowers planted directly in it without need for a flowerpot, so a waterproof liner is required. Copper is the best metal to use for the liner, as it is bent easily as well as being rust-resistant. However, both brass and galvanized steel also can be used. Cut out the liner according to the detail, fold as indicated and solder it. The wooden portion of the planter may be made of maple, or pine can be used and stained maple. To blend with more modern decor, the planter might be enameled and a decal added for the final touch. Two holes must be drilled near the upper edge of the planter back to permit hanging or fastening it to the wall. They are not shown on the detail. The ⅜-in. hole in the handle is a touch of realism, but can be used to screw the handle to the wall, if that is necessary.

Trellis-Type Shelf

The last shelf is of more conventional design and is simple to make. It consists of two 25-in. lengths of ½ x ¾-in. stock and one 28-in. length of the same material, that are used to form a vertical trellis to which three shelves are screwed. To provide an alternate design, the screws may be loosened and the back tipped at an angle, as indicated. ★ ★ ★

Fig. 2. Mixture of plant food and water is prepared for plants to promote normal growth in your absence

Save Your Plants While on Vacation

Fig. 1. An enclosure should never be placed over potted plant to reduce moisture evaporation. The plant would then be deprived of fresh air which is required for its survival and healthy growth

HOUSE PLANTS can't be taken along when you go on an extended trip. However, you can be assured that they will not only survive but remain in good condition during your absence, if given special attention before leaving as illustrated.

Remember that plants need fresh air just as much as they need water. Don't try to prevent evaporation of a plant's water supply by covering it with a glass enclosure as in Fig. 1. The plant will die for lack of air. If you have a terrarium, do not give it an oversupply of water since it has no provision for drainage, Fig. 6.

Fig. 4. Give plants their usual dose of supplementary food but no more than is required for one application

Fig. 3, below. Since most plants are accustomed to daily exposure to sunlight to carry on photosynthesis, remember to leave blinds partly open so as not to deprive them of this important requirement

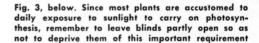

Fig. 5. Philodendron leaves are cleaned with wet, lintfree cloth to permit plant to "breathe" properly

Fig. 6. Since terrarium has no drainage facility, water is sparingly applied to avoid decay of plants

There are several ways of cleaning plant leaves, the easiest being simply to sprinkle a small amount of water on them with a rubber-bulb sprayer as in Fig. 7. Large leaves can be cleaned with a wet, lintfree cloth, Fig. 5.

A good way of reducing moisture evaporation from a potted plant, is to soak the soil and then insert a heavy cardboard disk in the top of the pot to fit around the stem or stems of the plant. For an absence of more than a week in hot weather, it is best to arrange to have your plants watered at least once a week. ★ ★ ★

Fig. 7. Rubber-bulb sprayer is ideal for washing dust from plant so that leaves "perspire" properly

PLASTER PATCHING

UNDERCUTTING

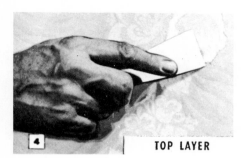

WETTING

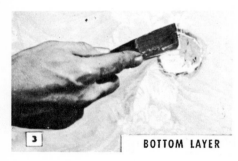

BOTTOM LAYER

TOP LAYER

SAND HIGH SPOTS

IT'S NO JOB at all to make minor plaster repairs such as filling cracks, "spotting" nail holes and sealing spaces between wood trim and plaster. Equally important is the occasional job of replacing loose plaster, especially in older houses. The time to make these repairs is just before repainting or wallpapering. Many remodeling jobs also require some plastering, which the average homeowner can tackle. However, major replastering jobs such as entire walls and ceilings call for the skill and experience of a professional plasterer.

Where to use Spackling putty: You use Spackling putty to fill cracks in plaster, from hairline size up to about ⅛ in. wide; in nail and screw holes around which plaster has not broken away; for nicks and surface imperfections in plaster, and for cracks that have developed between wood trim and plaster. To use the putty, first remove grease with strong washing solution and clean off all loose paint and dirt particles. A putty knife or wide scraper is handy for applying it and to smooth it on flat surfaces. At corners you can use a spear-shaped window-glazing tool, or just your finger protected with a rubber finger cot. Wipe off excess putty and smooth down the filling with a wet sponge.

Patching plaster: For cracks over ⅛ in. wide, and for areas up to about a foot or so square, use patching plaster. The powder is prepared by adding water and mixing to a smooth paste. Don't mix more than you can use before it starts to set—from 10 to 30 minutes depending on the product. Setting can be retarded by adding an equal amount of vinegar to the water used for mixing. Undercut the edges of cracks and small patches to make them wider at the bottom than at the top as in Fig. 1. This anchors the plaster in place. Next, brush away all loose particles and soak the old plaster, and plaster base if exposed, with water, Fig. 2, using a brush. Try to avoid

runs that may stain wallpaper. Wetting prevents rapid absorption of moisture from the patching plaster, which causes it to dry out too fast and crack away at the joints.

Press the plaster firmly against the under edges with the putty knife, Fig. 3. If the hole goes down to the lath, press the plaster down to key with the lath. Fill the hole, or wide crack, to ⅛ in. below the surrounding surface. If the hole is filled flush in one application, shrinkage of some kinds of patching plaster may cause a dish-shaped depression. Let the first application dry overnight, then wet the surface and complete the job, Fig. 4. If a nonshrinking type of plaster is used, fill the hole in one application. If the patch is too high when dry, dress it down with a coarse file (handle removed) or with sandpaper wrapped around a small block, Fig. 5. Seal the patch with thin shellac and allow this to dry before painting to prevent its showing up as a dull spot. If the adjoining wall surface has a sand-float finish, make the patch finish similar by adding an equal amount of clean, sharp sand to the last application, and pounce it with a piece of pile carpeting wrapped around a block.

Larger patches: When plaster bulges, particularly on ceilings where wood lath is used, and especially if it has been subjected to repeated soaking, chances are that it has loosened from the lath and is likely to fall off. Then the only remedy is removal of all loose plaster as in Fig. 6. Old plaster keys between the laths are pushed through, out of the way, so that the new plaster can key securely. Make the edges

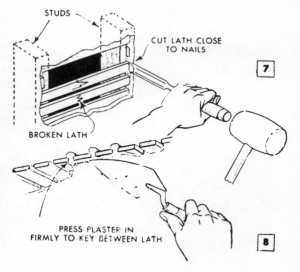

of solid plaster as regular in shape as possible—without jagged edges.

Sometimes the laths are loose; if so, nail them down solidly to joists or studs with lathing nails. If a lath has been pulled off, replace it. Broken laths are more likely to occur in walls crushed by heavy impact. In such cases the plaster is removed back to a stud on either side of the break and the broken pieces of lath are cut off midway on the studs with a chisel and mallet as in Fig. 7. This provides space to nail on new pieces of lath. Spacing between wood lath

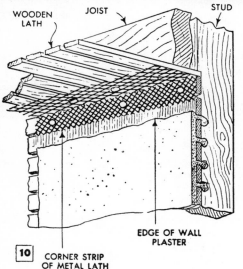

should be about ¼ in. If desired, you can use a piece of metal lath instead of wood lath, cutting it with tin snips and attaching it with ¾-in. staples.

Before patching, brush away all loose particles from the edges of the old plaster. Then wet the lath and plaster edges thoroughly. A pointing trowel or regular plasterer's trowel is more convenient to use in filling intermediate-size patches than a putty knife. A single, thick layer of patching plaster over lath, particularly on ceilings, often tends to sag. Therefore, after wetting the plaster edges and lath thoroughly, start by applying a layer to just cover the lath, pressing it down firmly to key it properly as in Figs. 8 and 9. After this has set, add more to build up the thickness until it comes ⅛ in. below adjoining plaster. Allow the plaster to dry overnight, then wet the surface and fill flush with a vinegar-retarded mixture so that you will have time to finish the surface properly. To match a smooth adjoining surface, use a trowel. To match a sand-float finish, add an equal amount of sand to the last batch of plaster and use a wooden float, Fig. 22, to even the surface. To get a surface level, check with a straightedge placed across the patch. While the filling is still soft, surplus plaster can be scraped off with the straightedge or with a wide metal scraper, moving it back and forth with a sawing motion while pushing it ahead. If adjoining surface is textured, allow the patch to dry, then apply texture paint as described under heading, "Covering unsightly walls."

For patches larger than a foot or so square, it's easier and more economical to use regular prepared plaster, application of which is covered under the headings, "Base-coat plaster" and "Finish coat."

Using trowel or float: When using a trowel or float for smoothing plaster, move it sideways, lifting the forward edge a trifle so it rides over the surface to avoid cutting into it. Keep the working surface of a trowel or float clean and smooth. When the finish surface starts to set, it can be troweled smooth and glossy by wetting the trowel a little, or running a wet brush ahead of the trowel as in Fig. 24. The float also should be dipped in water as necessary so that it won't adhere to and drag out soft plaster.

Covering unsightly walls: Old walls and ceilings that show many scars of previous patching jobs improperly done, may be restored to excellent appearance by covering with texture paint, provided the old plaster is securely attached to the lath. Texture paints, available in many tints, are of heavy consistency to permit filling low spots to produce a uniform surface. This may be pleasingly textured with brush marks, swirls, mottling with sponge or crumpled

WOODEN LATH — JOIST — STUD — EDGE OF WALL PLASTER

10 CORNER STRIP OF METAL LATH

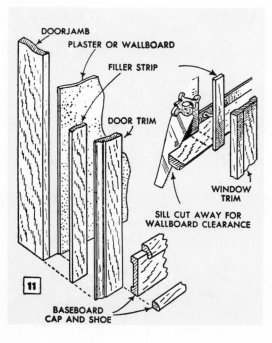

DOORJAMB
PLASTER OR WALLBOARD
FILLER STRIP
DOOR TRIM
WINDOW TRIM
SILL CUT AWAY FOR WALLBOARD CLEARANCE

11 BASEBOARD CAP AND SHOE

paper, or it can be stippled with a brush.

Replacing walls and ceilings: When loose plaster extends over large areas, it is probable that the entire wall or ceiling must be renewed for safety as well as for appearance. For a complete replastering job all old plaster must be removed; that between the laths is raked out or pushed back so spaces are open. If only a ceiling is replaced, a 2 or 3-in. strip of plaster is removed also from the top edge of walls as in Fig. 10. Strips of metal lath or ready-made corner strips are installed in corners to prevent cracks. The strips are fastened to studs and joists with large-head nails or long staples, spaced 6 in. where possible. You can do all this preparatory work and have a professional plasterer finish the job.

An unsightly ceiling, still tightly attached to the lath, can be covered with a new plastered ceiling if the supporting framework is strong enough to bear the added weight. Here, a plaster base of metal lath over furring strips, or self-furring metal lath, is installed, using washers and nails which are long enough to enter the joists about 1½ in. The nails should be spaced about 6 in. apart. Bend the lath to overlap walls where a narrow strip of plaster is removed, Fig. 10. Covering walls in this manner involves removing all trim and installing filler strips to bring door and window casings flush with the new plaster, Fig. 11. Considering this added work and expense, it may be better generally to remove the old plaster. In many cases, however, you can substitute ⅛-in. hardboard or ¼-in. wallboard for plaster, although this, too, requires the removal of trim and the addition of filler strips, Fig. 11.

Plaster bases: Either metal lath or gypsum lath is used for supporting plaster. Metal lath comes in sheets approximately 27 in. wide and 96 in. long. On large wall areas the sheets are run horizontally, the ends overlapped 1 in. and the edges about ½ in. Horizontal edges are held together with galvanized tie wire midway between studs. The sheets also are staggered so that the ends come on different studs or joists. Metal lath is nailed or stapled to these supports every 6 in., and is bent to fit inside and outside corners, running it past them to the next support to prevent corner cracks from developing.

Gypsum lath, Fig. 12, comes in 16 x 48-in. sheets, ⅜ and ½ in. thick. Some types are perforated to give a mechanical key besides the natural bond by suction. The sheets are nailed directly to studs and joists, or furring strips, with 1⅛-in. standard blued lath nails spaced 5 in. apart. For certain types of "floating" assembly, the lath is held by metal clips attached to studs and joists. Sheets are placed horizontally,

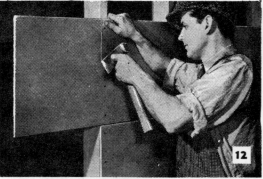

METAL CORNERS

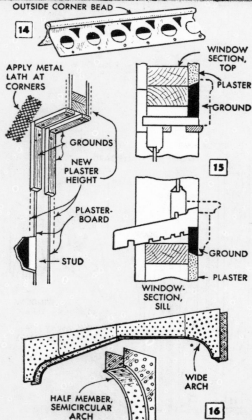
OUTSIDE CORNER BEAD

14

APPLY METAL LATH AT CORNERS

GROUNDS

NEW PLASTER HEIGHT

PLASTER-BOARD

STUD

WINDOW SECTION, TOP

PLASTER

GROUND

15

GROUND

PLASTER

WINDOW-SECTION, SILL

WIDE ARCH

HALF MEMBER, SEMICIRCULAR ARCH

16

17

face side out, and are staggered so that the ends will come midway on different nailing supports. Use gypsum lath only as a base for gypsum plaster. Reinforce the corners where two walls meet, or those where walls and ceiling join, with special corner covering or prebent strips of metal lath, Fig. 13. Reinforcing strips are provided also over the upper corners of doors and windows (Fig. 15) to prevent cracks.

Corner bead, grounds, metal arches: For outside corners over any type of plaster base, you use corner bead, Fig. 14. This protects the plaster against blows and also provides a "ground" to which plaster comes flush. The corner should come exactly to plaster height of both adjoining walls.

Grounds at door openings which are cut through an existing wall or partition are installed as in Fig. 15 and later removed. Permanent grounds are placed along window casings or nailed across studs to come just below the top edge of baseboards. Sometimes an additional one is installed at floor level. In many remodeling jobs, the old wall to which plaster is joined serves as a ground, and the other grounds are adjusted to this height. The edges of old plaster should be cut off as smooth as possible to make the joint inconspicuous.

Ready-mixed plaster: Prepared plaster is available in which the right ingredients are exactly proportioned by manufacturers, requiring only the addition of water. Always follow carefully the manufacturer's directions. Gypsum plaster should not be used on outdoor walls, concrete or asphalt coatings, or on walls subjected to much moisture. But it can be applied to clean brick or building tile.

Base-coat plaster: The standard minimum thickness of plaster for new construction is ⅝ in. over metal lath and ½ in. over all other lath. In remodeling jobs, new plaster should come flush with the old plaster to which it is joined. Plaster is applied in separate coats—one coat of base plaster over gypsum lath, but two over metal lath, followed by a finish coat in each case. If the wall is to be painted or papered, the finish coat may be omitted.

Mix the plaster in a watertight box with sloping ends, Fig. 20. Mix only as much plaster as you can use in an

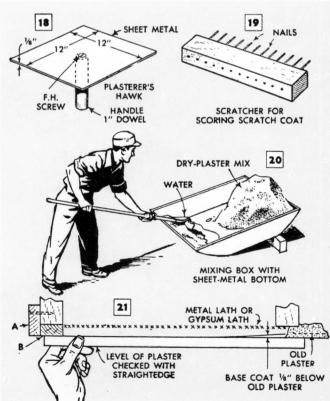

18 SHEET METAL

⅛" 12" 12"

F.H. SCREW

PLASTERER'S HAWK

HANDLE 1" DOWEL

19 NAILS

SCRATCHER FOR SCORING SCRATCH COAT

20 DRY-PLASTER MIX

WATER

MIXING BOX WITH SHEET-METAL BOTTOM

21 METAL LATH OR GYPSUM LATH

A

B

LEVEL OF PLASTER CHECKED WITH STRAIGHTEDGE

OLD PLASTER

BASE COAT ⅛" BELOW OLD PLASTER

hour. Don't add water after the plaster has started to set, and don't mix plaster of a previous batch with a fresh batch. Put some on a hawk, Fig. 18, and apply it with a plasterer's trowel.

When applying plaster to lath, press the first coat down and work it through the spaces of the wood lath, or mesh of metal lath, to obtain good keying, or to form good bond to gypsum lath. Then, cover the lath about ¼ in. Score crisscross grooves about ⅛ in. deep while the plaster is soft, using an improvised scratcher, Fig. 19. After the first coat has set hard, apply a second coat as in Fig. 17, to come flush with the ground. Where the new plaster joins old plaster, soak edges with enough water to prevent rapid absorption of moisture from the new plaster. Soak the edges of the old plaster either with a sponge or a brush. The plaster and lath should be soaked just prior to patching.

It's best to keep the base coat ⅛ in. below the surface of old plaster, where it joints, Fig. 21. Run the corner of the trowel along the old plaster edge, and then "wipe" the plaster with a trowel back slightly, returning gradually to the plaster height of other grounds. To get plaster level, use a straightedge across the grounds as in Fig. 21. For good adherence of a finish coat, the surface of the base coat should be slightly roughened by using a float, Fig. 22. Use a long float, Fig. 23, for large areas.

Finish coat: You can also buy prepared finish plaster. There are two kinds: smooth, trowel finish and sand-float finish for use with steel trowel or float respectively. The base-coat plaster must be hard when the finish coat is applied. If dried out, moisten the surface but do not soak. "Skim" on finish plaster in two applications, Fig. 25, producing a coat from 1/16 to ⅛ in. thick. As soon as the first application has set enough to prevent its wrinkling, skim on the second. When the plaster starts to set, give it a final troweling for a smooth, glossy finish, using a clean wet brush ahead of the trowel, Fig. 24, but use water sparingly. For an extra-hard surface, use Keene's cement in the proportion of 25 lbs. of dry, hydrated lime to 100 lbs. of Keene's cement.

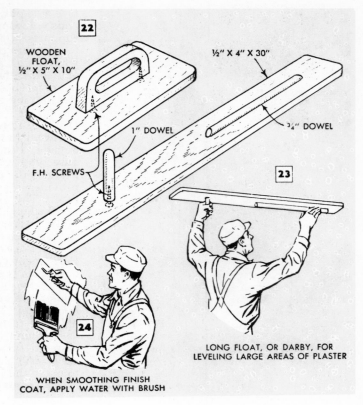

WHEN SMOOTHING FINISH COAT, APPLY WATER WITH BRUSH

LONG FLOAT, OR DARBY, FOR LEVELING LARGE AREAS OF PLASTER

(Some photos courtesy United States Gypsum Co.)

COVER IT WITH
STICK-ON PLASTIC

By Theodosia Carpenter

Makes many common household items take on a brand-new look. Adhesive backing lets it stick securely yet permits it to be peeled off like masking tape. Wipes clean with cloth

YOU'VE PROBABLY used masking tape and know how easily it can be peeled off. That's the way a waterproof decorative stick-on plastic works, except that a paper backing must be peeled off to expose the adhesive coating. The peeling feature makes the material exceedingly easy to apply—if you make an error in positioning it the first time, simply peel it off and start over. Or, if you wish to change to a new color scheme, just pull it off and begin anew. It can be applied to any smooth surface, adds a durable skin-thin layer of plastic and comes in rolls 18 in. wide. It can be obtained in peppermint stripes, gay kitchen and nursery prints, solid colors, wood grains and marble patterns.

When applying the plastic to a kitchen work area or marred table top, first fill deep scratches and gouges with wood filler and sand smooth

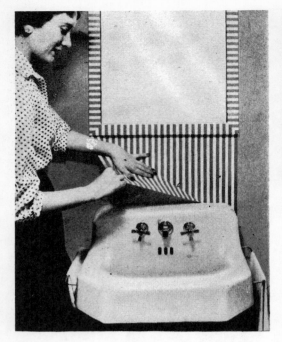

A candy-striped "bib" of stick-on plastic waterproofs and decorates the splash area of this washbowl. Note matching mirror frame in plastic

Plastic covering makes companion pieces of this wastebasket, talcum can and cleanser can. Below, no water, paste or tools are needed. Cut in the desired shape, remove backing and apply

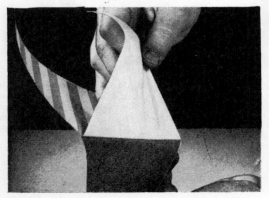

Printed designs are easy to cut from stick-on plastic and used like decals. Cut out before removing backing

One of several brands on the market is Con-Tact which is shown being applied in the photos. In the craft field, stick-on plastic can be used to transform many common articles into attractive pieces. A plain potato-chip can, for example, can be converted to an elegant bathroom wastebasket by covering it in a spiral pattern. The top and bottom are wound with white plastic clothesline glued in place. Matching pieces are a talcum-powder can and a scouring-powder can holder.

Stick-on plastic is excellent for covering books and magazines. In the time normally required to make a paper jacket, a book can be given a sturdy, permanent binding. The spine is covered first with a piece that extends well over the book covers. Matching or harmonizing pieces are cut about

Weathered and damaged sills take on new beauty when covered with wood-grained waterproof plastic

The numerous colors and patterns offered in the material afford a good covering for picture frames

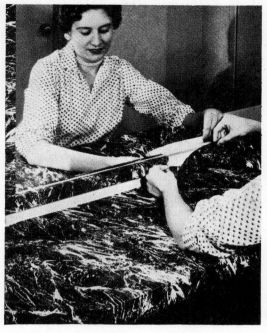

This marble pattern lends a distinctive note to the dressing table and gives it added serviceability

½ in. larger than the covers and stuck in place. Next the corners are mitered and the edges folded over. An appropriate pattern is used for end papers. If the book is coming apart, the end paper should extend both across the inside of the cover and the facing page.

Magazines are given a hard binding in much the same way. The front cover is cut off and a piece of cardboard of the same size substituted, while another is added on top of the back cover. After the binding has been attached, the magazine cover is pasted on the front.

Plastic coverings for kitchen tables are inexpensive and good looking. Working surfaces in the kitchen may be restored to a new appearance with the durable material. Its adhesive characteristic makes it especially useful for covering shelves and window sills.

Because it is waterproof, the product offers a wide variety of uses in the bathroom, as a splash covering around the washbasin or as a colorful frame on the wall around the medicine cabinet. The imitation wood grains are excellent for "paneled" dens or playrooms, while the patterned pieces make lasting washable wall coverings for bathroom and kitchen. ★ ★ ★

PLAYGROUND EQUIPMENT

Nontipping Swings for Gym Set

SEAT OF ⅝" PLYWOOD

A ladder salvaged from a dismantled windmill will make several nontipping swings for a home-built gym set. Several rungs are removed from each ladder section and a notched board is added for a seat. The swings are hung to the cross-pipe framework with rings formed of ¼-in. steel rod and later welded. Bolts in the pipe next to each ring provide stops to keep the swings from wandering sideways on the pipe. A dab of grease applied to the rings will make the swings noiseless, and a coat of paint will keep the swings from rusting.

Pipe Extension Lowers Swing Rope To Compensate for Slant of Limb

FLOOR FLANGE

½" PIPE

TEE

To make the ropes pivot at the same level when hanging a child's swing from the slanted limb of a tree, tie the outer rope to a pipe extension. Hung in this way, the swing will move in a straight arc. Cut a flat on the upper portion of the limb at the point where the outer rope is to be hung and drill down through the flat to permit inserting a length of ½-in. threaded pipe. Pass the pipe through the hole and fasten it with a floor flange as shown in the detail. Then turn a tee on the lower end of the pipe and tie the swing rope through the hole in the tee. The extension should lower the outer rope so that it pivots at exactly the same level as the inner rope.

Dr. Bernard Matzen, Napa, Calif.

Safety Ropes on Swing Prevent Sudden Falls

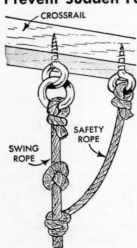

CROSSRAIL

SAFETY ROPE

SWING ROPE

Sudden falls from swings caused by breakage of the rope or a hanger can be avoided by installing auxiliary safety ropes as illustrated. Be sure to tie a knot in each swing rope immediately above the point where the safety rope is attached. Leave a little slack in the safety ropes to permit movement of the swing ropes.

THRILLS GALORE ON

HERE IS a miniature version of one of the most popular of amusement-park rides, the roller coaster. You can set it up in the back yard or basement in less than an hour, once the members for the track and supporting structure are cut and assembled into one straight and one contoured section as shown in the drawing and details. Slight slopes and a relatively short over-all length permit rides on the one-passenger car that are exciting for small children, yet completely safe. There are no curves or high track, and guide rails on both sections prevent the car from jumping the track. If a longer track is desired, a second contoured section may be added.

The car is of wooden construction with the front half of a roller skate screwed to the underside just forward of the front crossbar as shown in the detail. The other half of the skate is attached similarly at the rear of the car. Except for the ½-in.-plywood bottom, the car is made of 1-in. lumber as shown in the details. Exactly 5/16 in. clearance should be allowed between the track and the members nailed to the ends of the crossbars on the underside of the car as shown in the end view. These members, which serve as stabilizers, enable the car to glide over the track without tip-

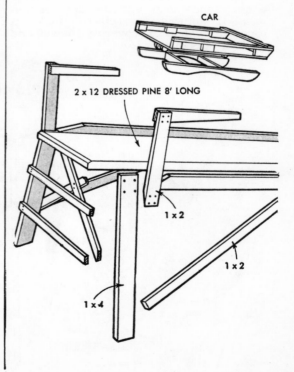

CAR

2 x 12 DRESSED PINE 8' LONG

1 x 2

1 x 2

1 x 4

THIS ROLLER COASTER

ping and prevent it from climbing over the guide rails. A footrest at the front of the car provides added safety.

For the straight section of the track, an 8-ft. length of 2 x 12-in. pine is elevated 2 ft. at one end by two 1 x 4-in. supports braced by four 1 x 2s. A bevel cut on the upper end of the track prevents the car from rolling forward when boarding it. The lower end of the track rests on a crossbar and the ends of the sideboards of the contoured section and is joined to the latter

section by two lag screws turned through the guide rails and into the 2 x 12.

After cutting the ¼-in.-plywood track for the contoured section, the pieces should be primed with linseed oil on both sides, then nailed to the sideboards and crossbars as shown in the details. Plywood or ½-in. lumber can be used for completing the contoured track. The guide rails should be well sanded and the car and track structure painted as desired to avoid injury from splinters and protect the wood. ★ ★ ★

Over-all length of track can easily be increased by adding one or more contoured sections for longer ride

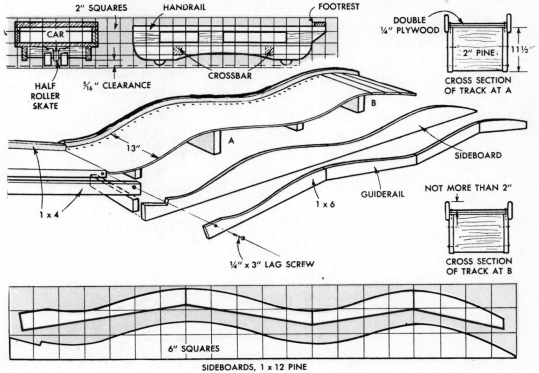

SIDEBOARDS, 1 x 12 PINE

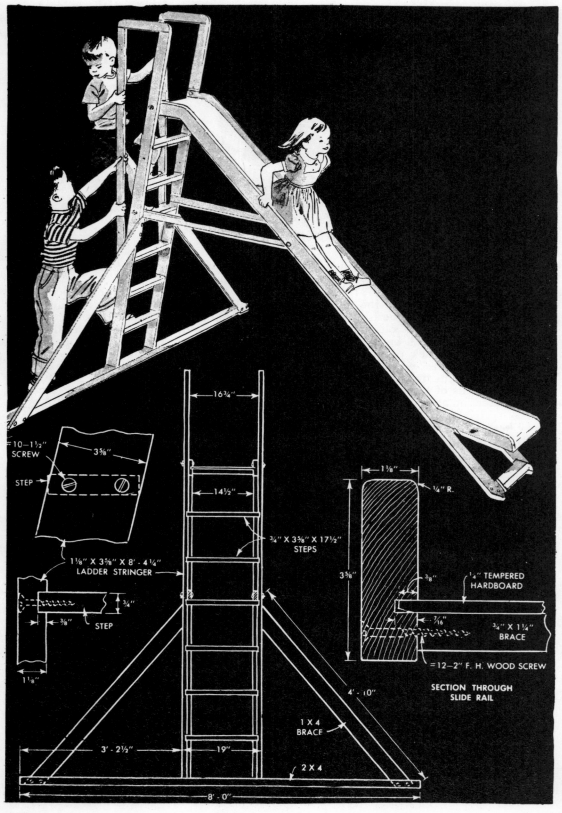

#10—1½" SCREW

3⅝"

STEP

1⅛" X 3⅝" X 8' - 4¼" LADDER STRINGER

¾"

⅜"

STEP

1⅛"

16¾"

14½"

¾" X 3⅝" X 17½" STEPS

1⅛"

¼" R.

3⅝"

⅜"

¼" TEMPERED HARDBOARD

7/16"

¾" X 1¼" BRACE

=12—2" F. H. WOOD SCREW

SECTION THROUGH SLIDE RAIL

4' - 10"

1 X 4 BRACE

3' - 2½"

19"

2 X 4

8' - 0"

Children's Slide

MATERIAL LIST

Tempered hardboard

1 pc. ¼" x 15¼" x 12' — Slide bed

Clear pine, redwood or cedar

2 pcs. — 1⅛" x 3⅝" x 14" — Top slide rails
2 pcs. — 1⅛" x 3⅝" x 10' - 4" — Side slide rails
2 pcs. — 1⅛" x 3⅝" x 25" — Bottom slide rails
2 pcs.—1⅛" x 3⅝" x 8' - 4¼"—Ladder stringers
2 pcs.—1⅛" x 3⅝" x 6' - ⅜"—Ladder handrails
2 pcs.—1⅛" x 3⅝" x 24"—Ladder handrails
2 pcs.—¾" x 3⅝" x 4' - 10"—Braces
2 pcs.—¾" x 1⅝" x 4' - 10"—Stay braces
1 pc.—1⅝" x 3⅝" x 14½"—Slide base
1 pc.—1⅝" x 3⅝" x 8'—Ladder base
2 pcs.—¾" x 3⅝" x 14½"—Slide cleats
7 pcs.—¾" x 1¼" x 14½"—Slide cleats
6—⅜" x 2½" carriage bolts
36—#10-1½" flat-head wood screws
30—#12-2" flat-head wood screws

Shrieks of delight from your youngsters will well repay you for the few hours it takes to build this junior-size back-yard slide. It is designed to be made from stock lumberyard material to eliminate unnecessary cutting, and ¼-in. tempered hardboard is used for the bed of the slide. The sectional detail through the rail of the slide shows how the hardboard is held in grooves and supported at intervals by 1 x 2 cross members. Where it is necessary to curve the hardboard at the top and bottom of the slide, the material must first be dampened for about 24 hr. to make the hardboard somewhat pliable. This is accomplished by placing wet cloths over the points of bend and keeping them wet for the required period. An application of varnish followed by wax will protect the bed of the slide and make it as slick as ice. Note that ladder assembly and braces are attached to the slide with bolts for dismantling when storing the slide during the winter

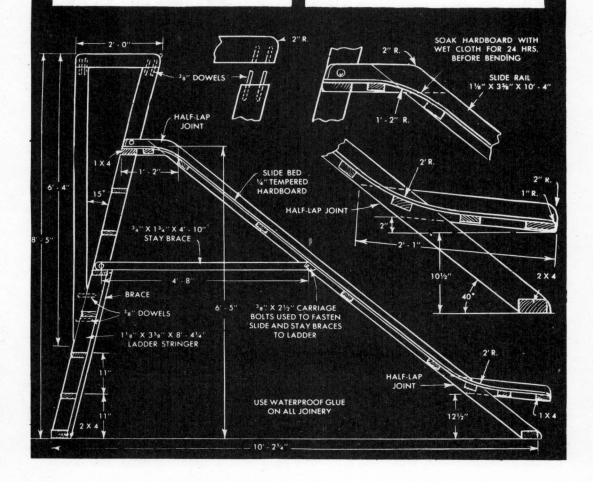

The tempered-hardboard slide surface is reinforced with 1 x 2-in. crosspieces spaced one foot apart

Swing Strength and Safety

Both strength and safety are designed into this swing that uses steel cable instead of rope. The upper ends of the cables are looped over thimbles welded between steel flats that are part of a welded assembly made from auto universal joints as shown in the right-hand detail. Cable clamps are used to secure the loops, and to provide stops on the lower ends of the cables. The stops bear against short lengths of pipe welded to steel angles. The angles are bolted to the seats, which are cut from 2-in. straight-grained stock. Lengths of rubber hose, slit lengthwise, are tacked to the front and back edges of the swing seats as another precaution against injury. To protect hands, lengths of rubber hose are slipped over the cables, to form grips, as in the left-hand detail. Brightly colored paints are used to make a "barber-pole" effect on the swing frame to make it more visible.—John O. Bock, Yakima, Wash.

COMBINATION

IF YOU HAVE youngsters between two and eight years of age, here is a combination slide and exerciser which will bring them hours of healthful fun. It dismantles into three easily handled sections so it can be moved indoors and set up in the basement playroom during the winter months. The whole unit is made of standard lumberyard material, consisting mainly of 1 x 2s and 2 x 4s, with hardboard being used for the bottom of the slide. All wooden parts should be protected with a coat of paint followed with two coats of spar varnish. Varnishing and waxing the hardboard will give a slick surface. ★ ★ ★

To provide maximum strength and avoid splitting of the members, pilot holes should be made for screws

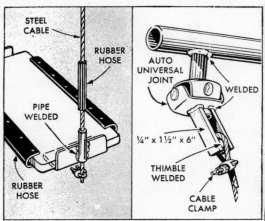

A summer-winter unit — comes apart in sections for setting up indoors when basement space permits

SLIDE AND EXERCISER

By Bob Brown

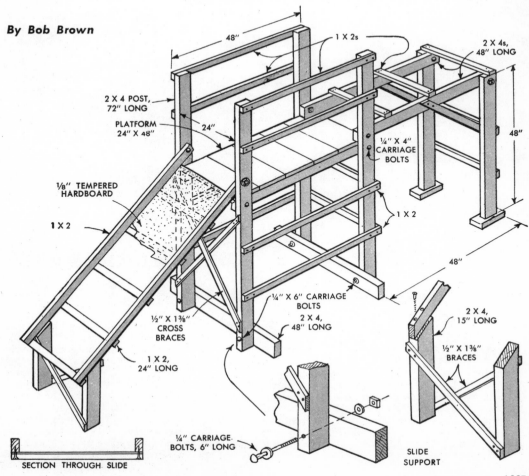

48"

1 X 2s

2 X 4s, 48" LONG

2 X 4 POST, 72" LONG

PLATFORM 24" X 48"

24"

¼" X 4" CARRIAGE BOLTS

48"

⅛" TEMPERED HARDBOARD

1 X 2

1 X 2

48"

½" X 1⅜" CROSS BRACES

¼" X 6" CARRIAGE BOLTS

2 X 4, 48" LONG

2 X 4, 15" LONG

½" X 1⅜" BRACES

1 X 2, 24" LONG

¼" CARRIAGE BOLTS, 6" LONG

SECTION THROUGH SLIDE

SLIDE SUPPORT

Deluxe Playhouse
has water and lights

By C. W. Woodson

ANY YOUNG LADY will feel like a fairy-tale princess when she is the proud owner of this enchanting playhouse that includes the modern magic of electric lights, running water and a heating plant. With the little house located in a corner of the back yard, Mother knows her daughter and friends are safely off the street, and she can check on the children's well-being in a moment.

Construction of the playhouse starts with staking-out the foundation, as shown in the detail at the bottom of page 1670. Assure that the main 6 x 8-ft. foundation is square by measuring the diagonals, both of which should be exactly 10 ft. Cedar posts 5 in. in diameter are cut in 2-ft. lengths (longer in areas of severe frost) and sunk in holes dug just inside the stakes as indicated in the upper detail on page 1670. Use a long

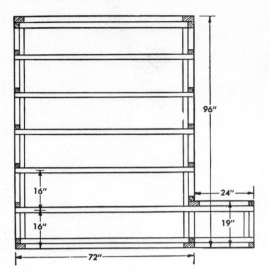

96"

16"

24"

16"

19"

72"

straightedge and level all the posts. A handful of gravel under a low post will bring it up to the right height. The foundation posts should project about 4 in. above the ground, which is high enough to permit ample air circulation under the building to prevent rot, while still being low enough for pleasing appearance. Sills, which can be either 4 x 4s or two 2 x 4s on edge, now are spiked to the foundation posts. Recheck the level of the foundation and shim up the sill where necessary. The floor joists next are toenailed to the sills. The joists are 2 x 4s on edge, and are spaced 16 in. on centers. After the first joist is nailed in place, a spacer block, lower right-hand detail, page 1671, can be used to speed work and assure accurate spacing. The joist plan at the left shows the joists in place and the location of wall studs that are spiked directly to the sills alongside the floor joists. Wall studs and roof beams are 2 x 2s, with the exception of the corner-post studs, which may be 2 x 4s, lower right-hand detail, page 1671, to provide a nailing surface for the interior wall covering. An alternate corner-post arrangement,

in which 2 x 2s are used, is shown in the right-hand center detail on page 1671.

Carefully check all details on page 1671 to familiarize yourself with the methods of framing the building, as well as noting the locations of openings for the door, windows and fireplace. The curved roof members of the projecting portion of the building—which can be used as a closet or storage area—are bandsawed from two pieces of solid stock. The fireplace opening in the back wall is as wide as the space between two wall studs and should be high enough to provide ample space for the electric heater that is to be installed in this area. The framing members over the

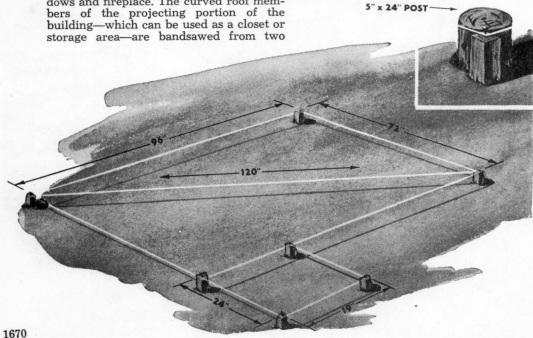

5" x 24" POST →

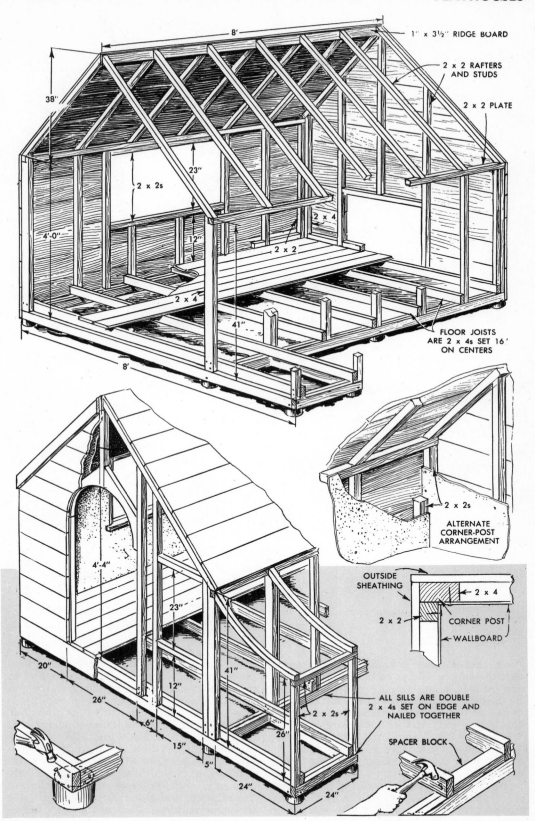

1" x 3½" RIDGE BOARD

2 x 2 RAFTERS AND STUDS

2 x 2 PLATE

8'

38"

23"

2 x 2s

4'-0"

12"

2 x 4

2 x 2

2 x 4

41"

FLOOR JOISTS ARE 2 x 4s SET 16' ON CENTERS

8'

4'-4"

23"

20"

26"

12"

6"

15"

5"

41"

26"

24"

24"

2 x 2s

ALTERNATE CORNER-POST ARRANGEMENT

2 x 2s

OUTSIDE SHEATHING

2 x 4

2 x 2

CORNER POST

WALLBOARD

ALL SILLS ARE DOUBLE 2 x 4s SET ON EDGE AND NAILED TOGETHER

SPACER BLOCK

FLOWER BOX
MAKE TWO SAME
LENGTH AS WINDOW SILLS

1" SQS.

door opening are bandsawed from solid stock, using a 13-in. rad., or the pattern for outside door trim on page 1673 may be used to determine the curve of the inner edges of the framing members. Note that the lower ends of these members are the width of a 2 x 2 on which each will rest. This provides a double 2 x 2 member on each side of the door opening for additional strength.

Tongue-and-groove sheathing is used for the floor of the playhouse, for roof planking and for wall sheathing. The sheathing goes on quickly and will assure a rigid structure. Around door, window and fireplace openings, the sheathing is applied so it is flush with the inside edges, as per details on page 1671. After the sheathing is applied, the chimney can be constructed. It consists of 1 x 8s fastened to cleats that are nailed to the sheathing. The rear face of the chimney then is nailed to the side pieces. The rear elevation of the playhouse detailed above shows the shape of the chimney, and indicates how the top of the offset in the chimney is shingled with the same material used on the roof. Imitation brick siding is used to cover the chim-

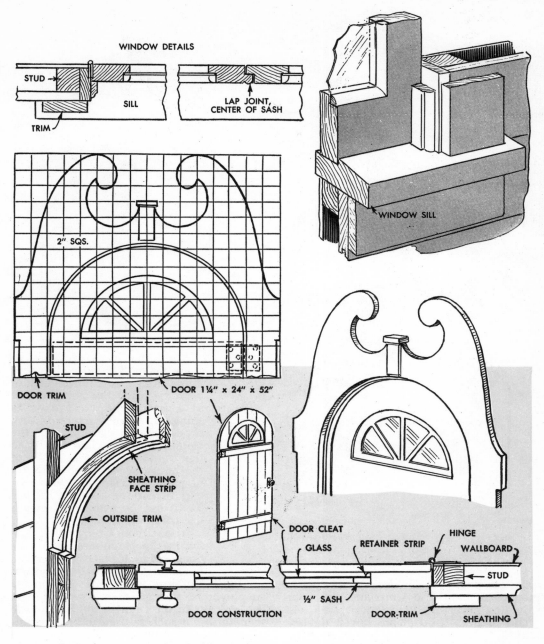

WINDOW DETAILS

STUD

SILL

LAP JOINT,
CENTER OF SASH

TRIM

WINDOW SILL

2" SQS.

DOOR TRIM

DOOR 1¼" x 24" x 52"

STUD

SHEATHING
FACE STRIP

OUTSIDE TRIM

DOOR CLEAT

GLASS

RETAINER STRIP

HINGE

WALLBOARD

STUD

½" SASH

DOOR CONSTRUCTION

DOOR-TRIM

SHEATHING

ney, and the top of the chimney is sealed against the weather by a sheet-metal or plywood cap. The latter is painted white to contrast with the red of the brick siding. Metal flashing is installed between the chimney and the roof, and also between the chimney offset and the sheathing.

Inside the chimney a horizontal plywood panel is installed just above the fireplace opening. It should be covered with metal so that it reflects the heat of an electric heater into the playhouse. The heater located in the fireplace is used to warm the little house on chilly days in early spring and late fall, permitting the house to be used a couple of months longer each year. To protect the lower edges of the chimney from ground moisture, it should rest on a stone or brick foundation.

Window-frame construction for the playhouse is detailed at the top of this page. If your workshop does not have facilities for building the window sash, it may be possible to use a stock window by altering the opening to suit, or a window can be ordered custom-built through most lumber yards. The double window on the side of the playhouse should be hinged to swing in,

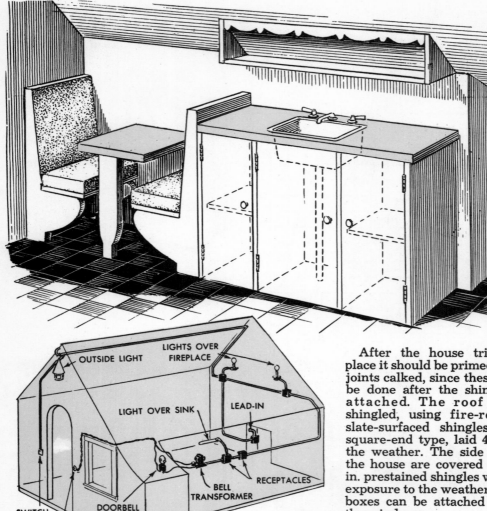

Wiring layout labels: OUTSIDE LIGHT, LIGHTS OVER FIREPLACE, LIGHT OVER SINK, LEAD-IN, SWITCH, DOORBELL BUTTON, DOORBELL, BELL TRANSFORMER, RECEPTACLES, WIRING LAYOUT

After the house trim is in place it should be primed, and all joints calked, since these cannot be done after the shingles are attached. The roof now is shingled, using fire-resistant, slate-surfaced shingles of the square-end type, laid 4½ in. to the weather. The side walls of the house are covered with 24-in. prestained shingles with 9-in. exposure to the weather. Flower boxes can be attached beneath the windows.

If local codes require it, wiring in the playhouse should be done by a licensed electrician, according to the diagram on this page. Running water and a drain for the playhouse sink are plastic garden hose. The sink set in the counter top is a plastic or metal basin such as used in house trailers and boats. Other built-in furniture can consist of a breakfast nook as shown in the illustrations, or toy furniture can be used. For ease of cleaning, the playhouse floor is covered with linoleum. Either hardboard or insulating wallboard can be used for interior covering of the walls. Both can be painted to provide a cheerful appearance and ease of cleaning.

Added luxuries, such as a radio, record player or television set can be added to the furnishings of the playhouse, depending on the age and interests of the residing princess. But no matter what the furnishings, childhood magic will be there. ★ ★ ★

while the single window beside the door is fixed permanently in its frame, the door providing necessary ventilation.

The arched front door, lower details, p. 1673, is built up from 1¼-in. clear pine strips glued edge-to-edge. Two cleats are glued and screwed to the inside surface of the door. The top of the door is rounded on a bandsaw and the fan-shaped window opening is cut out with a keyhole saw. A single piece of glass is fitted into this opening, divider strips and edge molding being cemented to the face of the glass and to the inside edge of the opening.

The scroll over the door is part of the outside trim and is cut from a single piece of plywood, using the squared pattern on page 1673. Straight trim is run from the lower edge of the arch to the door sill.

Photos by Don Honick

This little 6 x 8-ft. prefab, designed by The Masonite Corp., makes an exciting dream home for tiny tenants

TAKE-APART PLAYHOUSE

*Comes apart in easy-to-handle sections so it can be
set up indoors during winter for year-round play.
Made of durable hardboard, it takes paint beautifully*

A PLAYHOUSE is far from an inexpensive toy, but when it is designed for year-round play, it becomes less of a luxury when you consider the additional hours of fun it will afford your youngsters compared to other seasonal toys.

While it is true that a lot of basements will not permit setting up the house in its entirety, its take-apart feature makes it possible to erect a smaller version of the house where space is limited. The walls and roof panels are interchangeable like the parts of a construction toy so that just half the house can be set up for indoor play. Basement headroom will be of no concern in most cases as the total height

Modular panels make erection simple. Intermediate panels are interchangeable to vary window location

One lag screw anchors each panel to floor; two ¼ x 2½-in. carriage bolts fasten panel to panel

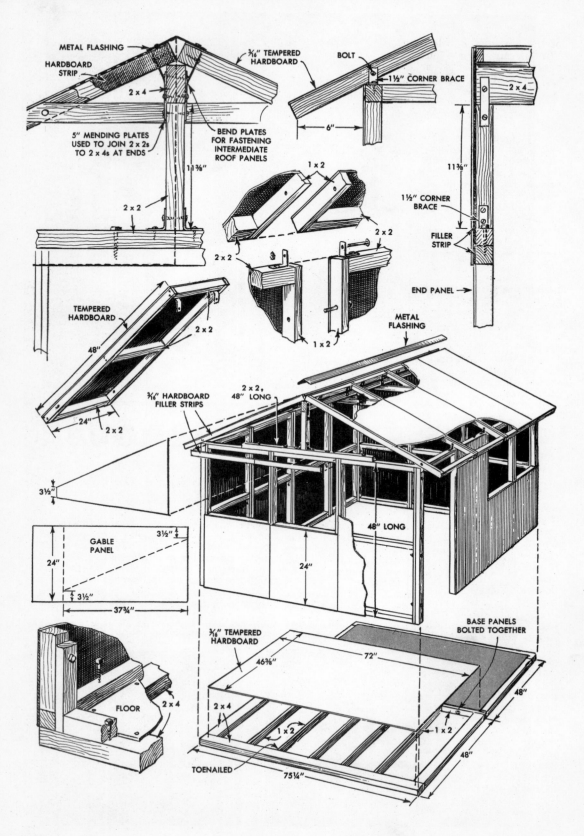

METAL FLASHING

HARDBOARD STRIP

2 x 4

5" MENDING PLATES USED TO JOIN 2 x 2s TO 2 x 4s AT ENDS

2 x 2

11⅜"

¾₆" TEMPERED HARDBOARD

BOLT

1½" CORNER BRACE

6"

BEND PLATES FOR FASTENING INTERMEDIATE ROOF PANELS

1 x 2

2 x 2

2 x 2

2 x 2

1 x 2

2 x 4

11⅜"

1½" CORNER BRACE

FILLER STRIP

END PANEL

TEMPERED HARDBOARD

48"

2 x 2

24"

2 x 2

METAL FLASHING

2 x 2, 48" LONG

¾₆" HARDBOARD FILLER STRIPS

48" LONG

3½"

GABLE PANEL

3½"

24"

24"

3½"

37¾"

FLOOR

2 x 4

BASE PANELS BOLTED TOGETHER

¾₆" TEMPERED HARDBOARD

46⅜"

72"

2 x 4

1 x 2

1 x 2

48"

48"

TOENAILED

75¼"

of the house is a little more than 6 ft. Window and door openings can be re-arranged, and screens and movable sash, as well as a door, may be added.

Framework of Stock Lumber

Except for the two floor panels which measure 4 x 6 ft., all others are made 2 x 4 ft. Counting the door panel, which really isn't a panel but rather a three-sided frame, you'll need 14 wall panels, including 4 corner panels, and 8 roof panels. The corner panels differ from the others in that a 2 x 2 is used along one side instead of a 1 x 2. Other than this, all panels are assembled exactly alike, using 2 x 2s for the cross members and 1 x 2s for the side members. These are nailed together to form simple frames which are covered on the outside with 3/16-in. tempered hardboard. Four of the panels are made half panels to provide window openings.

The two frames for the floor panels are assembled from 2 x 4s and 1 x 2s, the latter being set on edge and the 2 x 4s placed flatwise. The top sides are floored with hardboard. By ripping 1⅝ in. from the long side of two 4 x 6-ft. sheets, the hardboard will be just the right size to leave a 1⅝-in. border around the four sides.

Panels Bolted Together

Pick a level spot of ground to place the floor after bolting the panels to-gether from the underside. Start erect-ing the walls by fitting a corner panel first. As with all panels, a single lag screw in the center of the bottom rail is used to fasten the corner panel in place. Two bolts are used, one at top and bot-tom, to join each panel to the succeeding one. After the walls are erected, a 2 x 2 stiffening member, 48 in. long, is lag-screwed to the top of the end walls, bridging the center panels. This mem-ber supports the 2 x 2 posts that in turn support the 2 x 4 ridge board to which the roof panels are fastened with mend-ing plates. Angle brackets anchor the roof panels to the walls. Each gable end of the house is faced with two hardboard panels cut from a 2 x 4-ft. sheet. To make these overhang the covering on the wall panels and provide a drip edge, narrow filler strips of the material are first nailed to the outside edges of the end roof panels, the posts and the stiffen-ing members. The gable panels are fas-tened with roundheaded screws. Finally, the ridge is covered with a sheet-metal flashing, and 1 x 2 braces are installed on the inside of the house to join both halves of the roof. ★ ★ ★

Ridge board is supported at each end by 2 x 2 posts which are fastened to walls with metal angle brackets

Above, two 1 x 2 members are used to tie each side of the roof together after the panels are all in place. Below, individual roof panels are attached to the ridge board with screws and mending plates, the plates being bent

SCREW-HOLE PLUGS MADE FROM DOWELS

HERE'S A METHOD of making screw-hole plugs fast and in quantity. First, you drill blind holes to a uniform depth in a piece of waste stock. As will be seen, the depth of the holes determines the length of the plugs. Of course, the holes must be the same diameter as the dowel. Cut the latter into short lengths, each length slightly greater than the depth of the holes in the waste piece. Press the rough plugs thus made into the holes in the waste piece as in Fig. 2 and sand flush as in Fig. 3. Then split the waste piece into sections to release the plugs as in Fig. 4. To avoid damaging the ends of the plugs use a leather or soft-metal pad when tapping them into counterbored screw holes as in Figs. 1 and 5. Plugs made in this way are used to conceal screw and nail heads in boat construction, ranch-type flooring and cabinetwork. When plugs are used to conceal screwheads in ranch-type flooring they can be made from a contrasting wood, such as walnut or birch. Make them full length with a plug cutter, then finish to size as in Figs. 2 to 5 inclusive.

R. Hanscom, Elmhurst, Ill.

LEATHER OR METAL

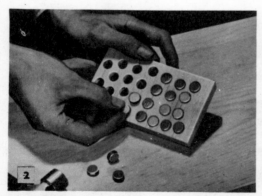

HOW TO PLAN YOUR PLUMBING SYSTEM

You CAN HAVE all the advantages of modern plumbing wherever running water under adequate pressure is available. The first step is careful planning, the second is selecting the right materials and the third is proper installation. The largest portion of a plumbing system is concealed from view and is normally impossible to reach after the walls and partitions are plastered. Fig. 2 shows the extent of the hidden piping of a plumbing system in a small house. Repair or replacement of this piping can be done only at considerable expense. Therefore the pipe, fittings and the workmanship should be of the highest quality.

Basic planning by homeowners: Basic planning in regard to the location of the fixtures, as well as their selection, is a job for the homeowner himself; the details of planning are generally left to an architect, building contractor or plumber. In planning you should consider possible future needs such as an extra bathroom, a basement shower, an outdoor sprinkling system, or in case you live in a rural district, branches to various buildings where water may be required. The installation can be done piecemeal. A layout carefully planned at the beginning makes it possible to do this without discarding, replacing or rearranging previously installed piping and equipment as new parts of the system are added.

Minimum plumbing for houses: Although home plumbing installations differ according to family requirements, it is generally considered that the minimum plumbing needs of the average small home should include a bathroom equipped with a lavatory, water closet, a bathtub having a shower outlet over it, an adequate kitchen sink, a suitable laundry tub and one or two outside hose connections. A combination sink for dishwashing and laundering is recommended only for very low cost homes.

Economy in new-house plumbing: Much greater flexibility in planning is possible when you are building a house than when you are installing plumbing in an existing

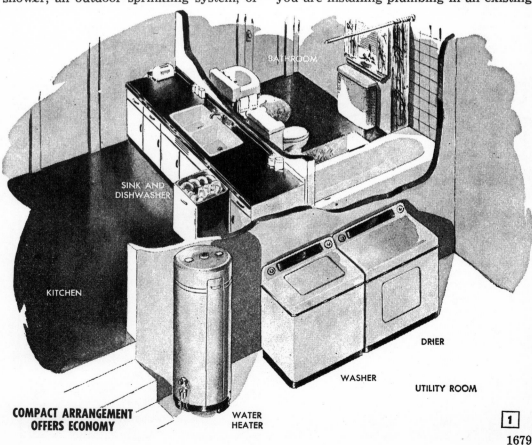

BATHROOM

SINK AND DISHWASHER

KITCHEN

DRIER

WASHER

UTILITY ROOM

COMPACT ARRANGEMENT OFFERS ECONOMY

WATER HEATER

1

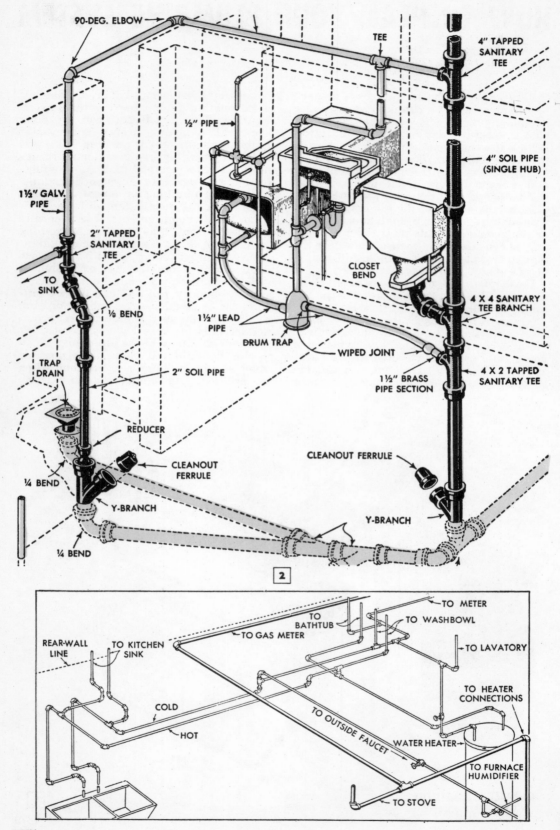

90-DEG. ELBOW

TEE

4" TAPPED SANITARY TEE

½" PIPE

4" SOIL PIPE (SINGLE HUB)

1½" GALV. PIPE

2" TAPPED SANITARY TEE

TO SINK

⅛ BEND

CLOSET BEND

4 X 4 SANITARY TEE BRANCH

1½" LEAD PIPE

DRUM TRAP

WIPED JOINT

1½" BRASS PIPE SECTION

4 X 2 TAPPED SANITARY TEE

TRAP DRAIN

2" SOIL PIPE

REDUCER

CLEANOUT FERRULE

CLEANOUT FERRULE

¼ BEND

Y-BRANCH

Y-BRANCH

¼ BEND

2

REAR-WALL LINE

TO KITCHEN SINK

TO BATHTUB

TO GAS METER

TO METER

TO WASHBOWL

TO LAVATORY

COLD

HOT

TO OUTSIDE FAUCET

TO HEATER CONNECTIONS

WATER HEATER

TO STOVE

TO FURNACE HUMIDIFIER

house. For economy in plumbing, rooms containing plumbing fixtures should be grouped together as much as possible and the piping installed in a common partition. For example, in a one-story basementless house, a minimum amount of material and labor are required if the bathroom fixtures are grouped on one side, and the kitchen sink on the other side of a partition. It is also wise to have this group of fixtures in close proximity to the utility room, as shown in Fig. 1.

Economy can be effected in the plumbing of a two-story house, such as shown in Figs. 3 and 4, by locating a bathroom directly above the first-floor bathroom and kitchen, with a common wall to enclose vertical pipes. In climates where severe freezing occurs, pipes should not be run in outside walls unless absolutely necessary and then only if the pipes are suitably insulated against freezing. Short hot-water lines supplying groups of fixtures not widely separated have an advantage over long lines in that only a small amount of water need be drawn off at the outlets before hot water becomes available. For longer lines the hot-water pipes should be insulated, which prevents water in them from cooling off quickly.

Bathroom suggestions: Six basic layouts for small and medium-size bathrooms equipped with bathtubs are shown in Fig. 3. The same arrangements are adaptable to larger rooms. Surplus space also can be utilized for cabinets, hampers or closets, or perhaps a counter in which a lavatory is installed. Detail A of Fig. 4 shows a 10 by 12-ft. room remodeled into a convenient bathroom equipped with a shower. Detail B shows a 12 by 12-ft. space used for a bathroom and for two closets of an adjacent bedroom, and detail C shows an alternate arrangement with wardrobe closets opening into the bathroom, in which case the tub and water closet are partitioned off from

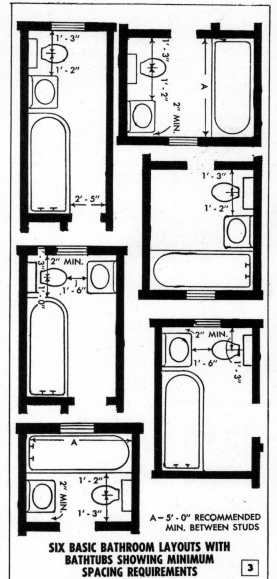

SIX BASIC BATHROOM LAYOUTS WITH BATHTUBS SHOWING MINIMUM SPACING REQUIREMENTS **3**

A – 5' - 0" RECOMMENDED MIN. BETWEEN STUDS

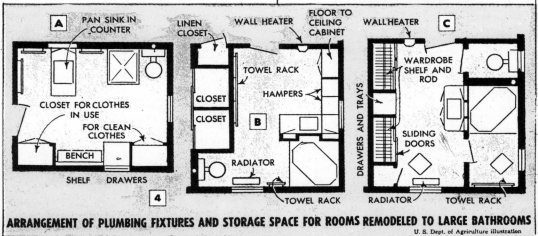

ARRANGEMENT OF PLUMBING FIXTURES AND STORAGE SPACE FOR ROOMS REMODELED TO LARGE BATHROOMS

U. S. Dept. of Agriculture illustration

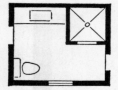

5

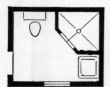

SHOWER STALL USED INSTEAD OF TUB IN SMALL BATHROOM PROVIDES MORE FLOOR SPACE, AND IN THIS CASE USE OF A VANITY-TYPE LAVATORY

HERE THE USE OF A CORNER SHOWER STALL WITH DOOR AT ANGLE IN CENTER OF ROOM GIVES MOST SPACE AND MAXIMUM CONVENIENCE IN SMALL ROOM

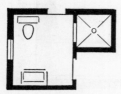

A SMALL BATHROOM CAN BE MADE LARGER BY UTILIZING ADJOINING SPACE SUCH AS A CLOSET FOR THE LOCATION OF A SHOWER STALL

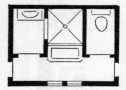

TWO-DOOR ENTRANCE TO THIS BATHROOM GIVES PRIVACY IN THE SHOWER STALL, YET PERMITS SIMULTANEOUS USE OF OTHER FIXTURES

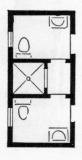

EXAMPLE OF GOOD PLANNING TO GET EQUIVALENT OF TWO BATHROOMS IN SMALL SPACE, A SINGLE SHOWER STALL BEING INSTALLED TO SERVE BOTH

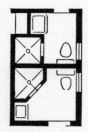

TWO SMALL BATHROOMS REPLACING A SINGLE LARGER BATHROOM WITH TUB, FOR THE GROWING FAMILY. BACK-TO-BACK ARRANGEMENT IS MOST ECONOMICAL

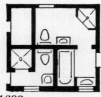

GROUP OF THREE BATHROOMS —A SEPARATE ONE ADJOINING A BEDROOM AND TWO WITH CONNECTING DOOR AND HALL ENTRANCE. INCLUDES TWO SHOWER STALLS AND BATHTUB

Henry Weis Mfg. Co.

6 LARGE BATHROOM DIVIDED BY PARTITION AND FIXTURES REARRANGED

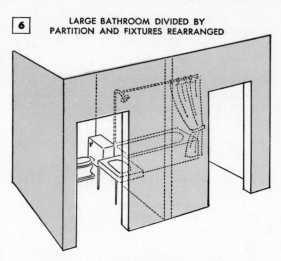

the lavatory. Shower stalls can be substituted for tubs. Seven arrangements for single and grouped bathrooms using shower stalls are shown in Fig. 5. When all the fixtures of a bathroom are arranged along one wall, less piping is needed. However, convenience and comfort should not be sacrificed for a relatively small savings in pipe costs. Fixtures for bathrooms can be obtained in a variety of colors.

If possible, a single bathroom should be located centrally in the house, where it is not necessary to cross another room to enter it. Bath and powder rooms should be located off a passageway where their entrances are not visible. They should not, if possible, open directly into a kitchen, living or dining room.

Adequate ventilation and lighting are essential. Try to arrange a lavatory at right angles to a window for maximum illumination from daylight. A window over a bathtub is not desirable as it is difficult to open and close by reaching over the tub. An extra shower curtain then is necessary to protect the window trim and curtain. A draft also is likely to be felt at times by anyone using the tub. If the window must be located over a fixture, and there is a choice, place it over the water closet so that the sill will come about 4½ or 5 ft. above the floor.

The door may be only 2 ft. wide if necessary. If possible, it should be located so that when opened it will conceal the water closet. The door should swing so that it will not strike anyone at a nearby fixture. If space inside of a bathroom is very limited the door can be swung out instead of in as customary. When fixtures are arranged on one wall, they should be spaced for sufficient elbow room.

A small bathroom is more easily heated than a large one. When a single large bathroom is used frequently by several mem-

7

Crane Co. photo

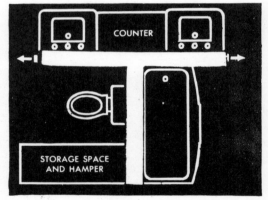

bers of a family, congestion can be relieved by dividing the room by means of a partition as shown in Fig. 6. One part can contain the bathtub or shower; the other the lavatory and water closet. Each is provided with a separate entry. A T-type bathroom, such as shown in Fig. 7, is another practical solution to relieve congestion in a home having only one bathroom. Note that there are two lavatories and a separate shower section. Although ample electric light should be furnished at the lavatory, preferably on either side of the wall cabinet or mirror, above it, no electrical outlets should be located within reach of a person in the bathtub as this involves danger to life.

Detailed planning: When a plumbing system is planned in greater detail than the approximate locations of fixtures, it is necessary to determine the arrangement and positioning of the piping. This is done by taking careful measurements in relation to the building construction. Before doing this, however, you should be thoroughly familiar with the method of assembling pipe, where and how to install vents, traps, etc. Also, the installation must conform to your local plumbing ordinance or "code." In the absence of a local code it is best to plan the installation according to the National Plumbing Code. When making your installation be sure to conform to the code and this will eliminate hazards from improperly installed plumbing. If you hire a building contractor or plumber to do the

work, even though you may help, it is his responsibility to plan the job according to your specifications, get a plumbing permit, make the installation meet all code requirements and then obtain local approval.

In case you are building a new house, the location of the plumbing fixtures and pipes should be indicated accurately on the plans, depending on how complete they are. Often however, the plumbing is not planned in detail and is left more or less to the discretion of the plumber. Lack of sufficient planning accounts for the frequent need of making expensive alterations by carpenters to provide space for the plumbing lines; also this negligence accounts for the incorrect installation of some plumbing systems. Therefore, planning the details beforehand often means a considerable saving of time and money.

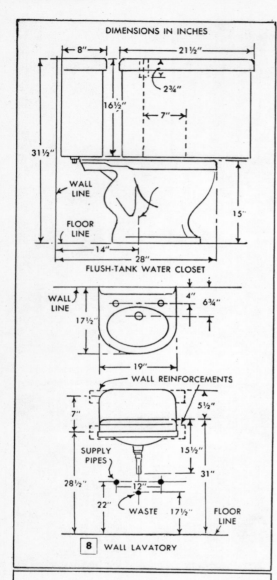

DIMENSIONS IN INCHES

FLUSH-TANK WATER CLOSET

8 WALL LAVATORY

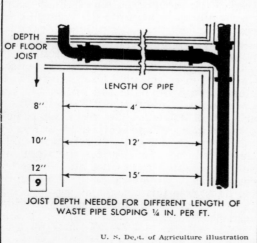

JOIST DEPTH NEEDED FOR DIFFERENT LENGTH OF
WASTE PIPE SLOPING ¼ IN. PER FT.

U. S. Dept. of Agriculture illustration

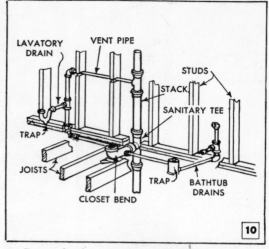

10

Since both water-supply and drainage systems connect to the fixtures, both systems should be planned carefully and coordinated in their relation to each other. You should either have the plumbing fixtures on hand when planning or have all the dimensions pertaining to them. The exact position of the supply and waste pipes, as well as the location of the fixtures, can then be accurately determined. Manufacturer's "roughing-in" sheets that accompany fixtures, and are sometimes available separately, supply this necessary dimensional data. Fig. 8 shows typical drawings and dimensions of roughing-in sheets.

Stack location: Since the soil and vent stack is the least "flexible" part of a plumbing system, and should be installed as close as possible to water closets and also centrally among other fixtures that it serves, its location should be determined first. The soil stack runs vertically and as nearly straight as possible from the house drain into which it discharges, and continues up through the roof for venting. It must be planned to avoid doors, heating ducts or pipes, girders under the first floor, electric-wiring outlets and dormers on the roof. The partition enclosing a stack must be wider than usual to provide sufficient space. Wider studs than usual can be used or regular ones furred out. The added space required varies with the size of the stack. It must be slightly greater than the outside diameter of the pipe at the hubs.

It may be necessary to choose a different location for water closets than originally planned to obtain better stack location. If possible, the horizontal lengths of soil pipe from the stack to the water closets should be run parallel to joists instead of across them. This saves cutting joists and installing extra floor framing. The width of the joists will limit the distance that a soil pipe at proper slope can be concealed between

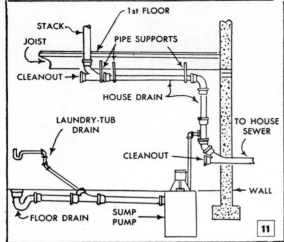

STACK
JOIST
1st FLOOR
PIPE SUPPORTS
CLEANOUT
HOUSE DRAIN
LAUNDRY-TUB DRAIN
TO HOUSE SEWER
CLEANOUT
WALL
FLOOR DRAIN
SUMP PUMP

11

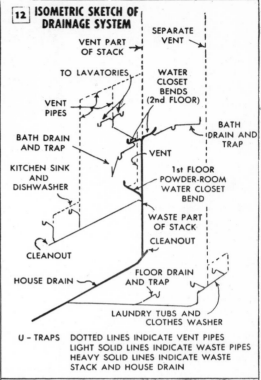

12 ISOMETRIC SKETCH OF DRAINAGE SYSTEM

VENT PART OF STACK
SEPARATE VENT
TO LAVATORIES
WATER CLOSET BENDS (2nd FLOOR)
VENT PIPES
BATH DRAIN AND TRAP
BATH DRAIN AND TRAP
VENT
KITCHEN SINK AND DISHWASHER
1st FLOOR POWDER-ROOM WATER CLOSET BEND
WASTE PART OF STACK
CLEANOUT
CLEANOUT
HOUSE DRAIN
FLOOR DRAIN AND TRAP
LAUNDRY TUBS AND CLOTHES WASHER

U – TRAPS   DOTTED LINES INDICATE VENT PIPES
LIGHT SOLID LINES INDICATE WASTE PIPES
HEAVY SOLID LINES INDICATE WASTE
STACK AND HOUSE DRAIN

stack and water closet as shown in Fig. 9.

After the stack location has been selected check the house construction, taking measurements if necessary to see whether the stack can be so installed. Also determine the position of the waste pipes, traps and the connections to stack and fixtures. Fig. 10 shows an arrangement which applies to a one-story house or to the second floor of a two-story house. Also determine the location of extra vents or waste stacks if needed.

Position of house drain: The house drain runs horizontally from the stack to the house sewer, generally at a slope of ¼ in. per ft., and connects to the latter about 5 ft. outside of the foundation wall. The house drain may be suspended from the basement ceiling, as in Fig. 11, or it may be run under the basement floor. The latter is usually preferred as it conceals the pipe and provides more headroom in the basement. In basementless houses, it is hung from joists above the crawl space or buried in a trench. In case the outlet of the house drain must be above the basement floor, as for example when a lower level would necessitate burying a septic tank too deep, or when a street sewer is higher than the basement floor, a sump pump is used to raise the waste from the floor drain and laundry tubs up to the house-drain level as in Fig. 11. The house drain should take the shortest straight path to the house sewer, avoiding unnecessary bends. Floor drain and tub waste connections must be carefully determined also. Cleanout plugs are provided to simplify clearing away obstructions if they should occur. These are located at the base of the stack or wherever the house drain changes in direction more than 45 deg. A cleanout should be provided for every 50 ft. of horizontal pipe.

Layout sketches: Next, make an isometric sketch of the drainage system like the

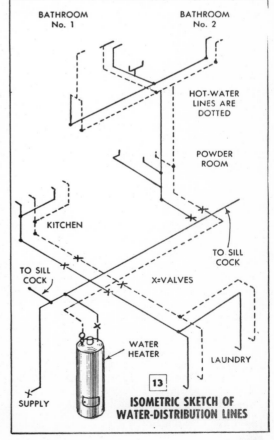

BATHROOM No. 1
BATHROOM No. 2
HOT-WATER LINES ARE DOTTED
POWDER ROOM
KITCHEN
TO SILL COCK
TO SILL COCK
X=VALVES
LAUNDRY
WATER HEATER
SUPPLY
13
ISOMETRIC SKETCH OF WATER-DISTRIBUTION LINES

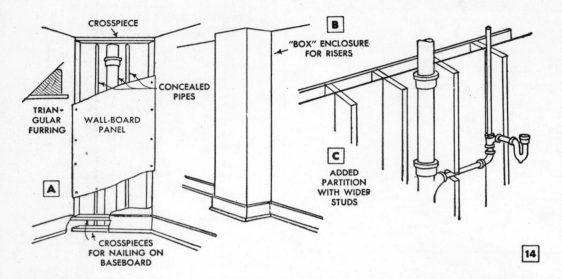

one shown in Fig. 12, entering all the connections and dimensions. This sketch provides a basis for ordering the material needed and also serves as a guide when making the installation. Such a sketch is easily made after ruling a number of light or colored guide lines at two opposite angles of about 30 deg., on which heavy lines to represent horizontal pipes are drawn. The vertical pipes are entered on the sketch by making vertical lines. Only one line is made for each pipe to indicate its center. Upturned "hooks" at waste pipes represent traps. Dotted lines indicate vent pipes.

A similar sketch is made of the water-supply and distribution system, Fig. 13, which you plan next. Because of the smaller size of pipes used, there is more flexibility of installation, although the connections to fixtures must be made at predetermined positions. In general the piping lines are grouped in the same or adjacent partitions if possible. The water-system sketch may have dots to indicate fittings in the pipe lines and X-marks to indicate valves. The sketch enables you to show horizontal pipes extending in any of four directions from vertical pipes and also show which way the openings face.

Before engaging in detailed planning of a plumbing system, it is best to become thoroughly familiar with installation of drainage lines and water-supply lines, some of the requirements covered may influence details of planning. Although you sketch the two systems separately, they should be planned in relation to each other so there will be no trouble of pipe interference.

Adding plumbing to existing houses: Concealed plumbing in existing homes is more difficult to install and also more costly

than in homes being built, but it is generally preferred in spite of its added cost. It will be necessary, however, to open floors and remove plaster. The best position of the stack is determined first. Location of bathroom and other plumbing fixtures will be influenced by stack location and vice versa. If a new wall is to be built to enclose the stack and water pipes, be sure to allow sufficient space. You can use 6-in. studs (actually 5½ in. wide) for a partition to enclose 3-in. soil pipe, if this size of stack is permitted in your locality. Sometimes a linen or clothes closet can be used to advantage for concealment of the stack and pipes. Another method is to group the pipes in a corner and conceal them with a panel of wallboard or plasterboard covered with plaster, which is joined to plaster on adjoining walls. Such an arrangement is shown in detail A of Fig. 14. Where pipes cannot be located in a corner they can be boxed in as in detail B. It is also possible to add a wider partition to one that is too narrow in order to accommodate the soil stack as shown in detail C. As plumbing fixtures are heavy, make sure that the floor joists are large enough to take the weight. Extra joists may be required.

Copper tubing used for water lines can be "snaked" through a closed partition, however, after first making sure that there are no obstructions. In such cases the partition is usually opened at the baseboard level of the first and second floors . In cases where minor obstructions in partitions prevent the use of rigid pipe, copper tubing is the best solution as it can readily be bent around such obstructions. However, rigid pipes can sometimes be installed in a partition by lowering them through the roof.

Installing or Replacing

SMALL WATER SYSTEMS

Careful planning and proper installation are vital for efficient and convenient operation

By Enno R. Haan

A S THE GREATER PORTION of a plumbing system usually is concealed, careful planning, good workmanship and the best quality of materials will minimize maintenance troubles, including possible replacement of pipe at considerable expense and inconvenience.

Adequate Pipe Size

Increased water demands occasioned by modern conveniences such as automatic dish and clothes washers, water softeners, air conditioners that use water for cooling and extra showers frequently tax a system beyond its capacity. Most plumbing complaints, outside those easily cured by minor repairs, generally are caused by undersize piping. Piping that is too small can cause whistling noises due to high water velocity, aggravate water hammer and permit backflow. The latter condition exists when undersize pipes restrict the flow of water so that if a faucet on the first floor of a house is opened, there is not enough volume of water to flow up to a faucet on the second floor. Often a partial vacuum will result in the piping on the second floor. Should a spray hose be connected to a faucet and dropped in the bottom of a filled bathtub, opening the faucet will permit the vacuum in the lines to siphon the water from the tub and discharge it through an open faucet on the floor below. The remedy for this condition is to replace the existing undersize piping.

Piping that was of adequate size originally, may become undersize because of lime and corrosion deposits inside. Another cause of insufficient flow and pressure in water pipe, which has the same effect as undersize pipe, is too many changes of direction in pipelines, involving an excessive number of fittings and often the wrong kind of valves. To determine the proper size to use is comparatively easy by following the

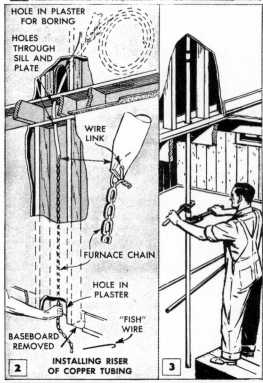

HOLE IN PLASTER FOR BORING

HOLES THROUGH SILL AND PLATE

WIRE LINK

FURNACE CHAIN

HOLE IN PLASTER

"FISH" WIRE

BASEBOARD REMOVED

INSTALLING RISER OF COPPER TUBING

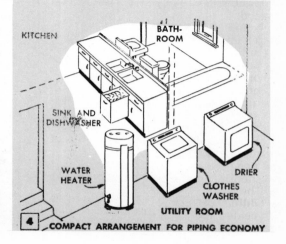

KITCHEN

BATHROOM

SINK AND DISHWASHER

WATER HEATER

CLOTHES WASHER

DRIER

UTILITY ROOM

COMPACT ARRANGEMENT FOR PIPING ECONOMY

A — WATER DEMAND

A—Rate of flow in gallons per minute (g.p.m.) per fixture
B—Estimated peak demand for each branch under conditions of simultaneous use

FIXTURE	A	B
2 sill cocks	10	5
Laundry tub	8	
Clothes washer	8	8
Kitchen sink	7.5	
Dishwasher	7.5	7.5
1st floor lavatory	5	
water closet*	3	
Bathroom No. 1		
lavatory	5	
water closet*	3	
shower	8	8
Bathroom No. 2		
lavatory	5	
water closet*	3	
bath tub	10	10
Total flow of all fixtures	83	
Peak demand for house		38.5

*Tank-type water closets

B — FLOW RATE AND REQUIRED PRESSURE FOR COMMON FIXTURES

FIXTURE	G.P.M.	P.S.I.*
Lavatory	5	8
Bath tub	10	5
Shower	8	5
Flush-tank water closet	3	12
Flush-valve water closet	15 - 40+	10 - 20+
Sill cock and 50 ft. hose	5	30

* Flow pressure per sq. in. at entrance
+ Due to design variations

C — APPROX. RESISTANCE TO FLOW OF THREADED FITTINGS, ETC., IN EQUIVALENT FOOT VALUES OF SAME-SIZE PIPE

FITTING OR DEVICE	½	¾	1	1¼	1½
90° elbow	0.9	1.3	1.8	2.2	2.7
45° elbow	0.6	0.9	1.2	1.5	1.8
Tee, side to end or reverse	2.2	3.4	4.4	5.5	6.7
Tee, end to end	0.7	1.1	1.5	1.8	2.2
Union or coupling	0.6	0.8	0.9	1.2	1.5
Globe valve	10.0	15.0	20.0	25.0	30.0
Angle valve	5.0	7.0	10.0	12.0	15.0
Gate valve	0.4	0.5	0.7	0.9	1 1
Swing check valve			3-20		
Vertical check valve			10-26		
H.w. tank, vert. 30-gal.		17.0			
H.w. tank, horiz. 30-gal.		5.0			
Water meter		14.0			

Water softener equals 50 to 200 ft. (if unknown use 125) 5

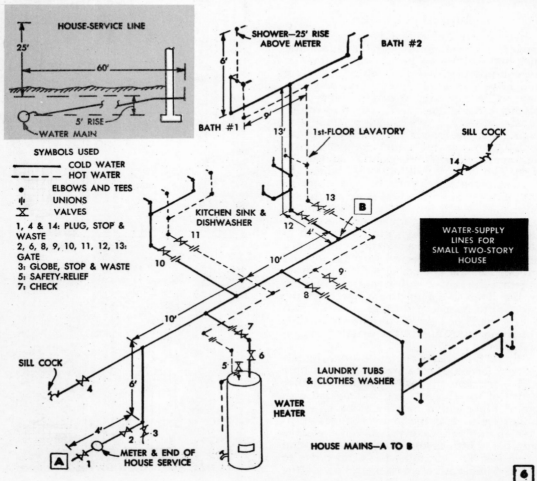

WATER-SUPPLY LINES FOR SMALL TWO-STORY HOUSE

SYMBOLS USED
— COLD WATER
--- HOT WATER
• ELBOWS AND TEES
UNIONS
VALVES

1, 4 & 14: PLUG, STOP & WASTE
2, 6, 8, 9, 10, 11, 12, 13: GATE
3: GLOBE, STOP & WASTE
5: SAFETY-RELIEF
7: CHECK

HOUSE MAINS—A TO B

6

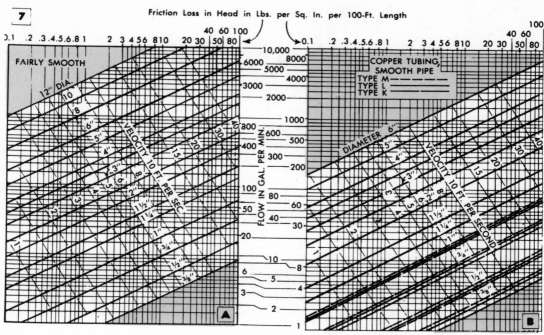

Friction Loss in Head in Lbs. per Sq. In. per 100-Ft. Length

Table C — STEPS OF PROCEDURE

Steps of Procedure	EXAMPLE (Refers to drawing and water-demand list) Object: To find required size of house-service line. 30 x .43=12.90
1. Multiply rise by .43 (weight of water 1 ft. high having a cross section of 1 sq. in.) This gives loss of pressure due to rise.	
2. Add 10 to finding of step 1. (10 is average minimum p.s.i. pressure for satisfactory flow at top outlet, not including a flush-valve type of water closet.	12.90+10=22.90
3. Find length of pipe from water source to highest and farthest outlet. (If water softener is to be used, add its pipe-equivalent resistance also, Table C, Fig. 5, when size of house service is figured.)	60+4+6+10+10+4+13+9+6=122 ft.
4. Subtract finding of step 2 from pressure at water source. Multiply result by 100 and divide by the finding of step 3. This gives approximate pressure loss (average) per 100 ft. of pipe, caused by friction.	Assume pressure at water main is 50 p.s.i. $\frac{(50-22.90) \times 100}{122}=22$
5. Locate finding of step 4 on or between vertical lines of Chart A or B, Fig. 7 (depending on pipe type). Locate peak demand on or between horizontal lines. If intersection coincides with, or is very close to a diagonal line, this line indicates proper pipe size to use. If intersection comes between diagonal lines, use next higher one.	Galvanized wrought-iron pipe is used. Refer to Chart A, Fig. 7. Locate 22 with vertical lines and 42 with horizontal lines. Intersection shows size pipe to use is 1¼ in.

procedure given in table C, Fig. 7. Information from the tables in Fig. 5 is used to determine factors that can be interpreted on chart A or B in Fig. 7.

Solving Installation Problems

Installing water lines in an existing house usually involves some difficulties. Where concealment of piping in an unobstructed partition is desired, one method is to use copper tubing, Figs. 1 and 2. When rigid pipe is used it can be cut in lengths of about 6 ft. and passed up through a partition from the basement, Fig. 3. Each length is screwed to another length by means of a pipe coupling. A cap is screwed to the upper end of the first length to protect the threads and keep out debris. To avoid removing more plaster than necessary when these methods cannot be followed, risers sometimes are run through closets where they are not conspicuous. Or, they are run up in a corner of a room and concealed with a panel. Cold-water lines in such locations should be insulated to prevent them from sweating when the warm air in the house contacts the cold pipe.

Short Pipelines

For economy and efficiency, pipelines should be as short as possible. Often risers that supply appliances in adjacent rooms, Fig. 4, can be run through a common partition. If hot-water lines are short, only a

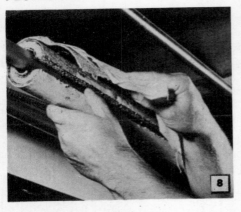

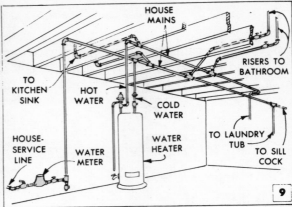

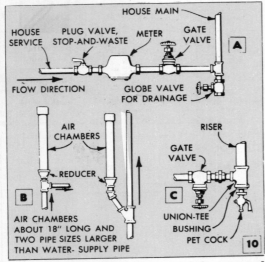

small amount of water need be wasted before hot water is available.

Where to Insulate Pipes

Insulation on hot-water lines, Fig. 8, prevents losses from heat radiation, prevents warming of adjacent cold-water pipes and makes hot water available quicker in frequently used lines. Usually hot and cold-water lines run parallel but not closer than 6 in. Do not install water pipes in outside walls unless absolutely necessary and then only if they are adequately insulated against freezing or, in warm climates, against heating. Use waterproof, antisweat insulation on cold-water pipes where water is likely to drip on plaster, furniture or tools, or where it can collect at the base of risers and cause rotting of a sill.

House-Service Line

The supply line from the water main to the house generally is buried 4 ft. underground to protect it from freezing and mechanical injury. It should be run as straight as possible, sloping toward the water main for drainage. It should never pass underneath a sewer line, it should be laid at least 12 in. above the top of the latter—always on compact, undisturbed earth. Generally, galvanized, wrought-iron pipe is used, although copper is more durable and is required by some building codes. The line should not be smaller than ¾ in. A plug-type, stop-and-waste valve often is installed at the house end.

House Mains

These lines, shown in Figs. 6 and 9, start at the service-line entrance and supply all branch lines. Horizontal lengths are supported at 5 to 8-ft. intervals, securely but not rigidly. A gate valve for shut-off purposes and a globe valve for drainage are installed as shown in detail A, Fig. 10. Pipe must have a slight slope for drainage, without sags, pockets and U-sections to trap water. Generally it is best to have the house mains the same size as the house-supply line. Pipe to a water heater or softener should not be less than ¾ in.

Branch Lines

Use gate valves to shut off branches individually. Globe valves are used only if there is surplus pressure, as they introduce considerable resistance to water flow. Pipes supplying two or more fixtures should not be less than ¾ in., and those to individual fixtures ½ in., although ⅜-in. pipe often is used for short runs to home lavatories or toilet flush tanks.

Air Chambers

Air chambers, which eliminate or reduce water hammer, are shown in details B and C, Fig. 10. For best results, air chambers in average home-plumbing systems should be about 18 in. long and two pipe sizes larger than the supply pipes to which they connect. Periodic renewal of the air which gradually is absorbed by the water compressing it, is done by "bleeding" the line. A drain petcock at each riser, detail C, permits this without shutting off the entire system. ★ ★ ★

PIPE FITTING

Do you want to replace a section of water pipe, change the location of a hot-water tank, or install a new plumbing fixture? Often you can save time and money by doing these simple plumbing jobs yourself. All you need are a few inexpensive tools and a knowledge of the essentials of pipe-fitting practice. It's easy when you know the right way to measure pipe and how to cut, thread and assemble it.

Correct measurements: Center-to-center measurements, which are necessary to lay out the job, are determined as shown in Fig. 1. The actual pipe lengths must be shorter than the center-to-center dimensions to allow for fittings and for the portion of the pipe that enters them. To determine exact lengths, subtract dimension A (center-to-face distance) of fittings from the center-to-center dimensions. Then add dimension C, Fig. 2.

The thread for a 1-in. pipe is not 1-in. outside diameter, as in other forms of thread. In piping, a 1-in. pipe has a nominal inside diameter of 1-in. with an outside diameter of 1.315 in. Another distinguishing difference between pipe threads and other forms of threads is that there is a ¾-in.-per-ft. taper in the diameter of the thread instead of a uniform diameter.

In modern pipe fitting, however, many materials are used, including copper, cast iron, wrought iron, etc. Copper piping has the advantage of a smooth bore and is easy to fit. The joints can be rapidly made, whether by compression, welding or soldering and the economy of labor costs thus achieved frequently outweighs the extra cost of copper as material. Wrought-iron piping properly protected from rust and corrosion with a coating of zinc is also much in favor, but should not be used in a district where soft water or water of an acid nature is apt to attack these metals.

If the handyman follows a few simple instructions, he should have no difficulty in making satisfactory pipe jointings.

Tools needed: Either of the vises shown in Fig. 6 will do, or you can use a machinists's vise fitted with detachable pipe jaws. You'll need two pipe wrenches for the average home plumbing jobs, an 8-in. and a 10-in. wrench. Using too large a wrench may result in buckling the pipe. The proper size wrenches for various pipe sizes are given in Fig. 6. You'll also need a pipe cutter, a reamer and a die stock with threading dies of the

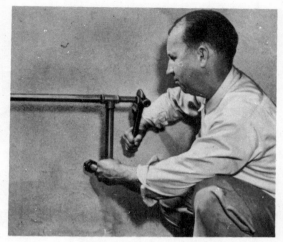

Jointing and attachment of piping, in either water supply or drainage, depends on the size of the piping and material of which it is made. Small-diameter wrought-iron pipes are usually tapped and joined with a threaded sleeve. Center-to-center measurements, which are necessary to lay out the job, are determined in the diagram of dimensions, below. The thread data is given in Fig. 2

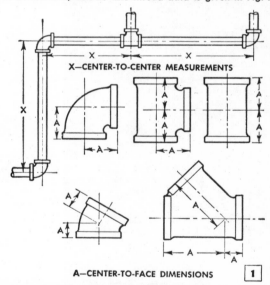

X—CENTER-TO-CENTER MEASUREMENTS

A—CENTER-TO-FACE DIMENSIONS [1]

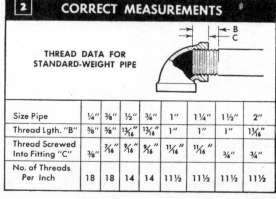

2 CORRECT MEASUREMENTS

THREAD DATA FOR STANDARD-WEIGHT PIPE

Size Pipe	¼″	⅜″	½″	¾″	1″	1¼″	1½″	2″
Thread Lgth. "B"	⅝″	⅝″	¹³⁄₁₆″	¹³⁄₁₆″	1″	1″	1″	1¹⁄₁₆″
Thread Screwed Into Fitting "C"	⅜″	⁷⁄₁₆″	⁹⁄₁₆″	⁹⁄₁₆″	¹¹⁄₁₆″	¹¹⁄₁₆″	¾″	¾″
No. of Threads Per Inch	18	18	14	14	11½	11½	11½	11½

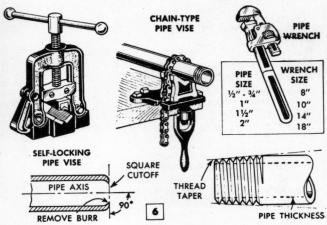

CHAIN-TYPE PIPE VISE

PIPE WRENCH

PIPE SIZE	WRENCH SIZE
½" - ¾"	8"
1"	10"
1½"	14"
2"	18"

SELF-LOCKING PIPE VISE

PIPE AXIS

REMOVE BURR

SQUARE CUTOFF

90°

6

THREAD TAPER

PIPE THICKNESS

3 CUTTING

4 REAMING

5 THREADING

sizes required. Cutting oil is used for lubrication and also to dissipate heat caused by the cutting action of the die.

Cutting off and reaming: Good pipe joints have the ends of the pipe cut off at 90 deg. to the axis, Fig. 6. It's best to use a regular pipe cutter, Fig. 3, rather than a hacksaw. First mark the pipe for cutting, not less than 1 in. from the end. Then grip it in the vise so that the mark extends far enough to permit the cutter and threading tool to clear the bench. Set the cutting wheel on the mark and screw the handle down so that the rollers rest firmly on the pipe. Apply cutting oil and proceed, screwing down the handle a little each time the cutter is rotated. When cut, use a reamer chucked in a carpenter's brace, as in Fig. 4, to remove the burr formed inside the pipe.

Threading: Pipe dies, Figs. 5 and 7, are held in a stock, which is fitted with handles for turning. The ratchet-type stock has only one handle. Ordinary pipe stocks hold dies of several different sizes. There are two types of dies—the solid, nonadjustable type and the split die, which is adjustable for wear and cutting depth. A different die is required for each size of pipe. In a stock-and-die assembly there also is a guide bushing—one for each pipe size within the capacity of the die stock, or one that is adjustable for size. The bushing slips on the pipe first and lines up the die on the end of the pipe. Pipe dies cut tapered threads

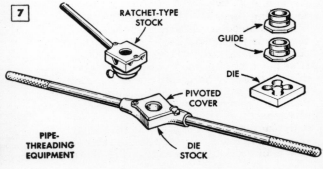

7

RATCHET-TYPE STOCK

GUIDE

DIE

PIVOTED COVER

PIPE-THREADING EQUIPMENT

DIE STOCK

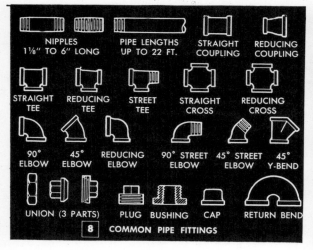

NIPPLES 1⅛" TO 6" LONG | PIPE LENGTHS UP TO 22 FT. | STRAIGHT COUPLING | REDUCING COUPLING

STRAIGHT TEE | REDUCING TEE | STREET TEE | STRAIGHT CROSS | REDUCING CROSS

90° ELBOW | 45° ELBOW | REDUCING ELBOW | 90° STREET ELBOW | 45° STREET ELBOW | 45° Y-BEND

UNION (3 PARTS) | PLUG BUSHING | CAP | RETURN BEND

8 COMMON PIPE FITTINGS

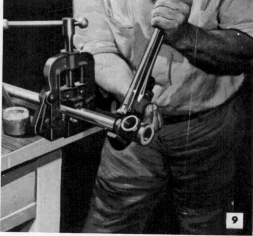

9

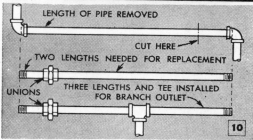

LENGTH OF PIPE REMOVED

CUT HERE

TWO LENGTHS NEEDED FOR REPLACEMENT

UNIONS

THREE LENGTHS AND TEE INSTALLED FOR BRANCH OUTLET

10

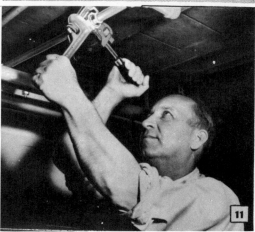

11

as in Fig. 6, and for this reason it is necessary to make sure that the die is placed in the stock so that the largest diameter faces the guide.

After slipping the guide bushing over the pipe, press the die teeth on the pipe slightly while turning the stock slowly to the right. Keep the handle at right angles to the pipe and apply a steady pressure until the die engages. Apply cutting oil liberally. Then start the thread by turning the stock forward a half turn and then back a quarter turn to break the chips. Now turn the stock slowly to avoid excessive heating, and apply cutting oil every two or three turns. Stop threading when the end of the pipe projects slightly beyond the small end of the die. This distance indicates that a thread of approximately standard length (dimension B of Fig. 2) has been cut.

Assembling pipe and fittings: Fig. 8 shows common pipe fittings you will use in an ordinary pipe assembly. Before assembling pipe and fittings, clean the threads with a wire brush to clear them of chips. Then spread pipe-joint compound on the threads of the pipe—never apply it to the internal threads of a fitting as it will be forced inside the pipe and may start an obstruction or taint the drinking water. Turn on a fitting by hand for three or four threads, after which a few more turns with a pipe wrench will draw it up snugly. Tighten the fitting on the pipe while it is still held in the vise, Fig. 9, and before threading the opposite end. This prevents accidental damage to threads and keeps the dirt out. It is not necessary to draw the fitting unduly tight. A moderate pressure on the wrench is sufficient. Excessive wrench pressure may distort the fitting or even strip the threads.

Replacing part of pipe: When a defective pipe is replaced, or when a new branch line is cut into an existing one, Fig. 10, it generally is necessary to saw the latter to permit unscrewing it except, of course, when there's a union to "break" the line. First shut off the water supply and drain the system by opening a faucet. Cut the pipe about 4 in. from a joint, never less if avoidable, and unscrew both pieces. The new section is made up of two lengths and a union, the total length of which should be equal to that of the old pipe. The same method is followed in installing a branch line, three lengths of pipe, a tee and a union being required. When tightening a union, Fig. 11, you'll need two wrenches to prevent the pipe from turning.

DRAINAGE SYSTEMS

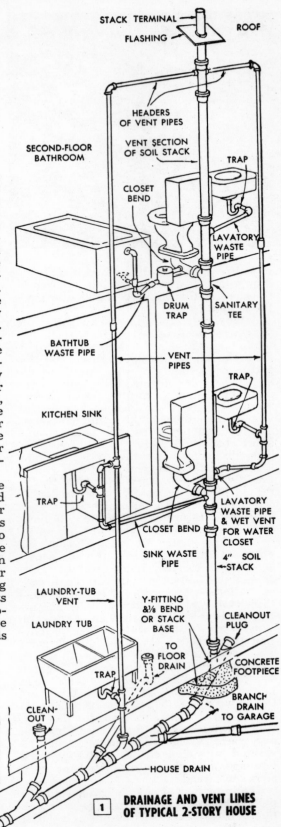

WHEN A COMPLETE home-plumbing system is installed, you start with the basic parts of the drainage system—the house drain and the soil stack—because the exact positioning of the stack and its relation to the spacing of the fixtures is of utmost importance. After installing the house drain and soil stack, the waste and vent lines must be coordinated carefully with the water-supply lines so that no interference will result.

What the drainage system includes: The drainage system consists of pipes that carry waste, and others that ventilate the system. Those carrying liquid waste but not the discharge from water closets are called waste pipes. Those carrying discharges from water closets are called soil pipes. Both convey their contents to the main soil stack or other stack, and these connect to the house drain, which is the lowest horizontal drainage line and connects to the house sewer. The latter starts at a point not less than 5 ft. outside of the house wall and leads to the city sewer or to the septic tank of an individual disposal system.

Stacks terminate above the roof. On some the lower portions serve for drainage, and the upper portion for ventilation; other stacks serve for ventilation only. Vent pipes which connect to drainage pipes are run to stacks by means of headers, at points above the highest fixtures. Traps are located in waste and soil lines near fixtures. Their purpose is to keep sewer gas from entering a building. Cleanout plugs at various points permit rodding drainage lines when obstructions occur. A typical home-drainage system comprising all of these parts is shown in Fig. 1.

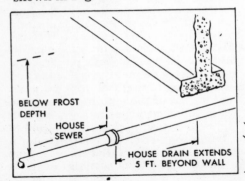

1 **DRAINAGE AND VENT LINES OF TYPICAL 2-STORY HOUSE**

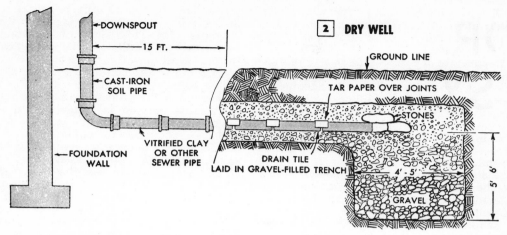

2 DRY WELL

DOWNSPOUT

15 FT.

CAST-IRON
SOIL PIPE

FOUNDATION
WALL

VITRIFIED CLAY
OR OTHER
SEWER PIPE

GROUND LINE

TAR PAPER OVER JOINTS

STONES

DRAIN TILE
LAID IN GRAVEL-FILLED TRENCH

4' - 5'

5' 6'

GRAVEL

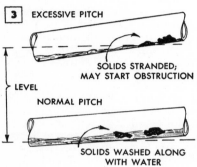

3 EXCESSIVE PITCH

SOLIDS STRANDED;
MAY START OBSTRUCTION

LEVEL

NORMAL PITCH

SOLIDS WASHED ALONG
WITH WATER

Kinds of drainage systems: A system used only to convey drainage from plumbing fixtures is called a sanitary system. A combination system also admits storm water. In many cities separate sanitary and storm-water drainage systems are required, each leading to a separate sanitary and storm-water sewer. The reason is that storm water in sewage is not desired where the latter is handled by a modern sewage-treatment plant. Storm water should never be emptied into a septic tank of an individual disposal system as it floods the tank and interferes with its operation. Storm water may lead to a dry well, as shown in Fig. 2, or to some other point of disposal. The discharge of storm water should be at least 50 ft. from any well, 20 ft. from an individual disposal field of sewage and at least 15 ft. from the house.

Pipe and fittings for drainage lines: Check with your local code concerning the kind of piping permitted for soil, waste and vent lines. Above-ground piping for soil and waste lines should be cast-iron, galvanized wrought iron or steel, lead, brass or copper. Vent pipes may be of these materials but asbestos-cement or bituminized-fiber pipe can be used often. For underground lines inside of a building, cast-iron pipe of the hub-and-spigot type is generally used, although galvanized wrought-iron or

steel, lead and copper pipe may be permitted also. Where threaded joints are approved for underground use, they should be coated with asphalt enamel and wrapped with a suitable waterproof material. Storm drains and house sewers may be cast iron, copper, vitrified clay, concrete, bituminized fiber or asbestos cement.

Threaded fittings should be of the recessed drainage type, although ordinary cast-iron fittings may be used on vent pipes. Long-radius fittings are used in drainage lines wherever possible to make gradual changes of direction, particularly in horizontal lines. Any fitting that has an enlargement, chamber or recess with a ledge, shoulder or reduction of pipe area, which can obstruct the drainage flow, should not be used in any drainage line. Increasers in vent stacks and 4 by 3-in. closet bends are not considered restrictive fittings.

Pipe slope or pitch: In drainage lines the flow of liquid is entirely dependent on gravity. For this reason horizontal sections of drainage lines must be given a uniform slope or pitch, which may vary from ⅛ to ½ in. per ft., depending on the pipe size and conditions encountered. The pipe must not have any dips or pockets from which sewage cannot drain out completely. Threaded fittings that connect horizontal pipes to vertical ones have their horizontal openings pitched at the usual slope of ¼ in. per ft. Care must be taken to install them correctly.

For pipes 3 in. or less in diameter, the slope should not be less than ¼ in. per ft. For larger sizes of pipe a slope of not less than ⅛ in. per ft. is sometimes used. However, where conditions necessitate a lesser slope, it should be such as to assure a flow of not less than 2 ft. per second. Excessive slope in horizontal pipes, particularly in large-size pipes, allows solids to remain in the pipe while the water drains away, as in Fig. 3. When a house drain must be installed above a basement floor, water from the laundry tubs and basement floor drains is pumped up to it with a sump pump.

Importance of correct pipe sizes: For minimum cost as well as efficiency, use the smallest pipe sizes that will adequately carry away sewage. Installing a house drain larger than required does not increase its efficiency as may be supposed, because the flushing action of the water is greatly decreased in a large pipe, leaving solids stranded. See Fig. 3. However, if the pipe is too small it will be overloaded, which may occasion troubles such as basement flooding and back pressure in the drainage pipes.

Basis for finding pipe sizes: The fixture-unit system is used to determine pipe sizes for both drainage and vent lines. The basic unit is 7½ gal. per minute flow (approximately 1 cu. ft.), this being the amount of water discharged from the average type lavatory. Multiples of this unit are used to express the discharge rate of various fixtures as given in Fig. 4, which also gives the minimum sizes of traps for these fixtures. Table B gives fixture-unit discharge of various sizes of pipe openings, and is used for tanks and for fixtures not listed in table A.

Sizing house drain and sewer: To find the size of a sanitary house drain and sewer, you add up the fixture units to get the total load and then refer to table C of Fig. 4. For example, if the total load of a system is found to be 30 fixture-units, reference to the table will show this value to lie between 27 and 216 in the column for ¼-in. slope, which is most generally used. Using the higher value, the proper size pipe would be 4 in. This method is similarly followed for branch lines. Generally the house drain and main stack are the same size. A 3-in. size for these is generally adequate for most small homes. A pipe smaller than 3 in. should not be used to take the discharge of a water closet. No portion of underground drainage branches should be less than 2 in. in diameter.

Sizing combination and storm-water drains: Where storm water can be discharged into a combination house drain or sewer, you allow one fixture unit for each 180 sq. ft. of roof area discharged into the house sewer. This value is based on rainfall rate of 4 in. per hour. The total roof load is added to the fixture-unit load. Arrangement of an outside storm drain is shown in Fig. 5. It should run in the same horizontal plane as the combination drain or sewer and be connected to it with a single Y-fitting at least 10 ft. downstream from any branch to the house drain or from any soil stack. To determine the size of pipe re-

A

A DISCHARGE RATES OF FIXTURES IN FIXTURE UNITS

Type of Fixture	Fixture-Unit Value	Minimum Size of Trap (In.)
One bathroom group consisting of water closet, lavatory and bathtub or shower stall		
for tank-flushed closet	6	
for flush-valve closet	8	
Shower stall		
Bathtub (with or without shower head)	2	2
Lavatory	2-3*	1½ - 2
Kitchen sink	1-2*	1¼ - 1½
Kitchen sink with disposal unit	2	1½
Dishwasher	3	1½
Combination sink and laundry tub	2	1½
Combination sink and laundry tub with disposal unit	3 4	1½ Separate traps 1½
Laundry tub (1 or 2 compartments)	2	1½
Water closet—tank-flushed	4	3
Water closet—flush-valve type	8	3
Floor drain+	1	2

* Depends on size of outlet; see table B
\+ Size determined by area of drainage

B

FIXTURE UNITS AS RELATED TO DRAIN SIZE

Size of Drain or Trap (In.)	Fixture-Unit Value
1¼ or smaller	1
1½	2
2	3
2½	4
3	5
4	6

Note: For a continuous or semicontinuous flow into drainage system, as from a pump, add two fixture units for each gallon per minute of flow

C

MAXIMUM FIXTURE-UNIT LOADS FOR HOUSE DRAINS AND SEWERS, INCLUDING BRANCHES

Pipe Dia.	⅛" Slope	¼" Slope	½" Slope
2"		21	26
2½"		24	31
3"*	20	27	36
4"	180	216	250
5"	390	480	575
6"	700	840	1000

*Not more than two water closets

D

MAXIMUM FIXTURE-UNIT LOADS FOR STACK AND HORIZONTAL BRANCHES

Pipe Dia.	Any Horizontal Branch	When Connected to One Stack Not Over 3 Stories High
1¼"	1	2
1½"	3	4
2"	6	10
2½"	12	20
3"*	20	30
4"	160	240
5"	360	540
6"	620	960

* Not more than two water closets

4

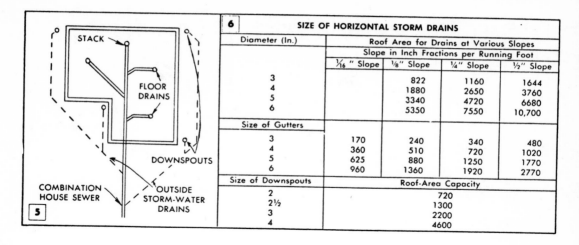

6	**SIZE OF HORIZONTAL STORM DRAINS**			
Diameter (In.)	Roof Area for Drains at Various Slopes			
	Slope in Inch Fractions per Running Foot			
	1/16 " Slope	1/8" Slope	1/4" Slope	1/2" Slope
3		822	1160	1644
4		1880	2650	3760
5		3340	4720	6680
6		5350	7550	10,700
Size of Gutters				
3	170	240	340	480
4	360	510	720	1020
5	625	880	1250	1770
6	960	1360	1920	2770
Size of Downspouts	Roof-Area Capacity			
2	720			
2½	1300			
3	2200			
4	4600			

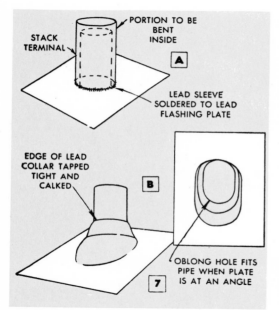

quired for storm drains, gutters and downspouts, refer to the table, Fig. 6.

The soil stack: A soil stack is run up inside of the house generally, being concealed in partitions if possible. It should be centrally located so that the drainage and vent lines serving various fixtures will be of minimum length. It is not advisable to place a stack in an outside wall in climates where temperatures drop to freezing and below, unless the pipe is sufficiently insulated. For the same reason, and also because of appearance, a stack is usually not located outside of a building. In mild climates, however, this can be done to minimize cost, and the stack then can be boxed in for concealment. A soil or waste stack should not be smaller than the largest horizontal branch connected to it, although a 4 by 3-in. water-closet bend is not considered a reduction in pipe size. To determine the proper size of the stack consult table D, Fig. 4.

Stack and vent terminals: A stack passing through a roof should project no less than 6 in. above it. Leakage at the roof is prevented with lead or copper flashing as in details A and B of Fig. 7. Detail A shows vent flashing made by soldering a lead sleeve over a hole cut in a sheet of lead. The angle between the sleeve and sheet should correspond to the roof pitch. The extending end is bent down inside of the pipe. Detail B shows a formed flashing which has an oblong hole so that the flashing can be set at various angles, after which the collar is tapped to a snug fit against the pipe. Shingles go over a flashing sheet at its highest portion, but go under it at the lowest portion.

Provisions must be made to prevent the moisture inside of the stack terminal from freezing and possibly clogging it. This trouble is less likely on 6-in. extensions than on longer ones. Where possibility of such frost closure exists, the terminal should be at least 3 in. in diameter, though 4 in. is preferable. Small vent stacks should be enlarged by means of increasers such as shown in Fig. 8A. They are joined to the stack a foot or so below the roof. Another precaution against frost closure is insulation between the pipe and the flashing as in detail B, or by providing an air space which is heated from the building as in detail C.

The terminal of a stack or vent pipe should not extend directly beneath a door, window or other ventilating openings of a building. If within 10 ft. of such an opening, the vent should project at least 2 ft. above it. When a vent terminal is extended horizontally through a wall, where permitted, it should be at least 10 ft. from the lot line and the opening should face downward. A vent should never terminate under the overhang of a roof or under any other part of a building.

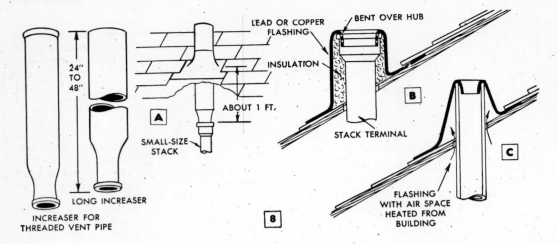

LEAD OR COPPER FLASHING
BENT OVER HUB
INSULATION
24" TO 48"
ABOUT 1 FT.
STACK TERMINAL
A
B
SMALL-SIZE STACK
LONG INCREASER
FLASHING WITH AIR SPACE HEATED FROM BUILDING
C
INCREASER FOR THREADED VENT PIPE
8

Offsets in stacks: Sometimes a stack, located advantageously in relation to the fixtures it serves, cannot be run up in a vertical line as is most desirable, owing to building construction or other interference. In such cases it is necessary to go around the obstruction with an offset. A single offset, as in Fig. 9A, introduces less resistance than a return or jumpover offset as shown in detail B. An offset in the drainage portion of a stack, which is 45 deg. or less from the vertical, is sized as a straight stack, but in case a horizontal branch connects within 2 ft. above or below the offset, a relief vent is installed. This may be either a vertical continuation of the lower portion of the stack, detail C, or it may be a side vent connected between the offset and the next lower horizontal branch. See detail D. In either case a vent is also provided above the offset as in detail E.

The size of the vents should not be smaller than the main vent or half as large as the stack. If an offset is below the lowest horizontal branch and is greater than 45 deg. from the vertical, its size is determined as for a building drain. A horizontal branch should not connect to a stack within 2 ft. of an offset that is greater than 45 deg. from the vertical. These restrictions do not apply to offsets in the vent portion of a stack.

Horizontal drainage branches: A drainage extension to a water closet should be as short as possible and not less than 3 in. in diameter. A cast-iron water-closet bend may be plain or may have tapped openings for connecting waste pipes from fixtures. The size of a waste pipe from an individual fixture is the same as the minimum trap size for the fixture, as given in table A of Fig. 4. Waste pipes serving more than one fixture must be sized according to their fixture-unit load, referring to table D of Fig. 4. An example of sizing horizontal

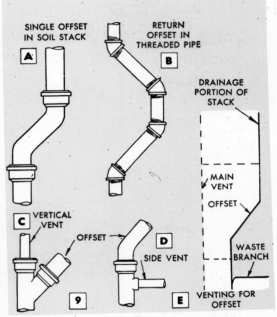

SINGLE OFFSET IN SOIL STACK
A
RETURN OFFSET IN THREADED PIPE
B
DRAINAGE PORTION OF STACK
MAIN VENT
OFFSET
C VERTICAL VENT
OFFSET
D
SIDE VENT
WASTE BRANCH
9
E
VENTING FOR OFFSET

waste pipes of a bathroom group is shown in Fig. 10. Sometimes larger sizes are used for waste pipes serving one or more fixtures, as for instance when the waste pipe is vented from a stack located too far from the fixture to use the normal size. See "Stack venting" discussion that follows.

Purposes of vent pipes: In every plumbing installation the drainage system requires vent pipes for three purposes: (1) To prevent the water seal in fixture traps from being sucked down into the drain pipe either by siphon action or by the momentum of the discharge flow; (2) To prevent back pressure, particularly at lower levels, from forcing water out of traps through the fixtures and (3) to carry away sewer gases to the outside of the house.

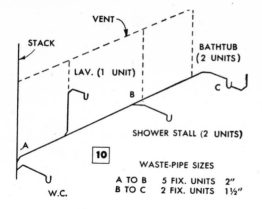

VENT

STACK

LAV. (1 UNIT)

BATHTUB (2 UNITS)

B

C

SHOWER STALL (2 UNITS)

A

10

W.C.

WASTE-PIPE SIZES

A TO B	5 FIX. UNITS	2"
B TO C	2 FIX. UNITS	1½"

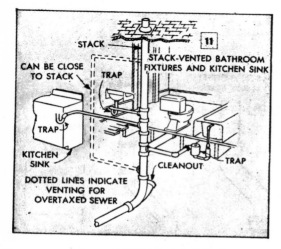

STACK

11

STACK-VENTED BATHROOM FIXTURES AND KITCHEN SINK

CAN BE CLOSE TO STACK

TRAP

TRAP

KITCHEN SINK

CLEANOUT

TRAP

DOTTED LINES INDICATE VENTING FOR OVERTAXED SEWER

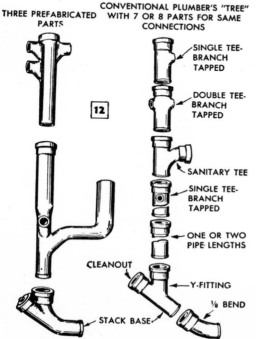

THREE PREFABRICATED PARTS

CONVENTIONAL PLUMBER'S "TREE" WITH 7 OR 8 PARTS FOR SAME CONNECTIONS

12

SINGLE TEE-BRANCH TAPPED

DOUBLE TEE-BRANCH TAPPED

SANITARY TEE

SINGLE TEE-BRANCH TAPPED

ONE OR TWO PIPE LENGTHS

CLEANOUT

Y-FITTING

⅛ BEND

STACK BASE

Stack venting: The simplest and most economical venting installation for a group of fixtures often used in single-story houses or at the top floor of two-story houses, is "stack-venting," shown in Fig. 11. This is applicable for the following conditions:

(1) The distance from the stack to the fixture traps is limited as specified in the table, Fig. 14. If a fixture is located too far from the stack to vent it through waste pipe of a size based on fixture units, a larger diameter waste pipe that meets the requirements of distance, as given in the table, Fig. 14, can be used.

(2) No other water closet or bathtub can discharge into the stack at a higher level.

(3) The total discharge of the fixtures above the water closet and bathtub connections to the stack must not exceed three fixture units.

(4) Each of the fixtures must discharge into the stack independently of others.

When a sink connects to a stack-vented bathroom group at a location where the street sewer occasionally becomes overloaded and floods the house sewer, a relief vent should be connected to the stack below the stack-vented water closet or bathtub, as shown by the dotted lines in Fig. 11.

Prefabricated stack-venting units: Time and money can be saved by using prefabricated drainage units designed for stack venting where their use is permitted by local code. These units are neat and compact and can serve the drainage requirements of kitchen sink, laundry tub and even a bathroom group of fixtures in a one-story house. All of them, of course, should be located close to the stack according to requirements. Various arrangements of fixtures are possible. Fig. 12 shows three prefabricated units that replace seven or eight ordinary pipe lengths and fittings of the usual plumber's "tree," used for the same purpose. The vent portion of the stack in

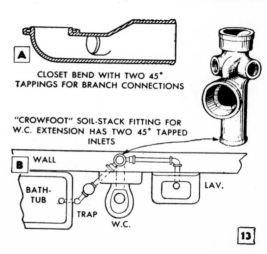

A

CLOSET BEND WITH TWO 45° TAPPINGS FOR BRANCH CONNECTIONS

"CROWFOOT" SOIL-STACK FITTING FOR W.C. EXTENSION HAS TWO 45° TAPPED INLETS

B

WALL

BATH-TUB

TRAP

W.C.

LAV.

13

MAXIMUM DISTANCE OF FIXTURE TRAP FROM VENT	
Size of Fixture Drain	Distance in Feet
1¼"	2½
1½"	3½
2"	5
3"	6
4"	10

14

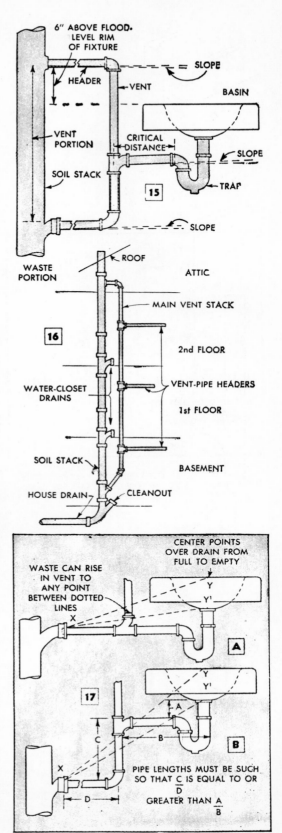

this case may be a 2-in. galvanized-steel stack, screwed to the top of the upper unit and provided with an increaser to prevent frost closure where it extends above the roof. Fig. 13A shows a tapped closet bend and detail B shows a "crowfoot" stack fitting that has two 45-deg. tappings for waste branches; detail also shows an application.

Back vents: When fixtures are too far from the stack for stack venting, as is the case with the arrangement shown in Fig. 10, they are back-vented. This is also required when a water closet, bathtub or shower discharges into the soil stack above them even though they may be close enough to it for stack-venting. The basic idea of venting a fixture is shown in Fig. 15. The vent pipe extends from the top of the drain pipe, vertically or at an angle of not less than 45 deg. from the horizontal. The distance from the vent opening to the crown weir of the fixture trap (see Fig. 22A) is somewhat critical and should not be greater than specified in Fig. 14. It should not be less than two pipe diameters. Also, vent opening should not be below the weir.

When a long-sweep outlet of a fitting serves as a vent opening, Fig. 17 A, point it in the direction of the fixture discharge. The vent pipe may connect either to the vent portion of the soil stack or to a separate stack by means of a horizontal pipe called a header, which should be sloped so that moisture collecting in it from condensation will run toward the stack or the drainage pipe. The connection of a header to a waste or soil stack should be made at least 6 in. above the flood-level rim of the highest fixture draining into the stack.

Main vent stack: When fixtures at different heights require venting, it is customary to run headers to a main vent stack, which generally is located close to the soil stack. See Fig. 16. The lower end of the main vent stack may connect to the soil stack or to the house drain; its upper end may terminate above the roof independently, or it may be connected to the vent portion of the soil stack. A vent header should connect to a main vent stack no less than 6 in. above the flood-level rim of highest fixture it serves.

Dry and wet vents: Vents such as shown in Figs. 10 and 15, which are used only to admit air to waste pipes, are called "dry" vents. They should be arranged so that the

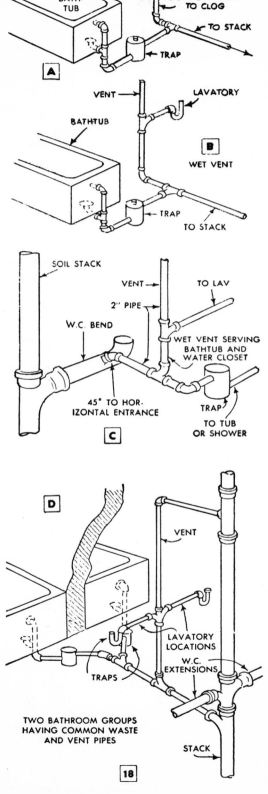

waste discharge from a fixture cannot rise into the vent opening. This would allow deposits from the discharge to build up and eventually clog the opening. Fig. 17A shows a lavatory vent that is apt to clog because it falls below the lines, XY and XY1, which extend from the center points over the drain when the basin is full and empty, to the point where the waste pipe joins the stack. Waste that is being discharged from a fixture can rise to any point between these lines in a vent pipe connected too close to the trap. Detail B shows a similar lavatory installation in which the pipes are arranged so that the vent opening comes above the lines XY and XY1.

Detail A of Fig. 18 shows a dry vent of a bathtub installation where it is usually impossible to obtain a drop in the pipe as just described. In such cases the customary method of venting consists of connecting the waste pipe of a vented fixture, such as a lavatory, to the bathtub drain—as shown in detail B. Then one vent serves for both fixtures. The lavatory discharge washes away deposits that may collect from the bath discharge. The section of pipe serving for drainage as well as venting is called a "wet" vent. A slightly different arrangement is shown in detail C. Detail D shows an installation of two bathrooms, side by side, where both tubs are wet-vented by the common vent for both lavatories.

The drain from a back-vented kitchen sink or other fixture may be similarly used as a wet vent for a bathtub or shower. In all of these cases, a 1½-in. wet vent should not serve as a waste line for more than one fixture unit and a 2-in. wet vent for not more than four fixture units. Also, the horizontal waste branch should connect to the stack at the same level as the water-closet drain, or just below it, when installed on the top floor. It may also connect to the water-closet bend. On lower floors, the same arrangement requires a 2-in. pipe for the wet vent and its waste extension to the stack. Also, each water closet below the top floor then should be individually back-vented unless the 2-in. wet vent connects directly to the water-closet bend at a 45-deg. angle to the horizontal portion of the bend and in the direction of flow as shown in detail C of Fig. 18.

Diameters and lengths of vent pipes: Pipe used for venting should never be less than 1¼ in. in size nor less than one half the diameter of the drain pipe it vents. A vent stack or the venting portion of a soil stack should not be less than one half the diameter of the soil stack. Generally the vent portion of a soil stack is the same size as its drainage portion, but in many small one-story houses the vent portion may be of reduced size if permitted by local code.

SIZE AND LENGTH OF VENTS   19

Size of Soil or Waste Stack (In.)	Fixture Units Connected	Diameter of Vent Required (In.)						
		1¼	1½	2	2½	3	4	5
		Maximum Length of Vent (Ft.)						
1¼	2	30						
1½	8	50	150					
1½	10	30	100					
2	12	30	75	200				
2	20	26	50	150				
2½	42		30	100	300			
3	10		30	100	200	600		
3	30			60	200	500		
3	60			50	80	400		
4	100			35	100	260	1000	
4	200			30	90	250	900	
4	500			20	70	180	700	
5	200				35	80	350	1000
5	500				30	70	300	900
5	1100				20	50	200	700
6	350				25	50	200	400
6	620				15	30	125	300
6	960					24	100	250
6	1900					20	70	200

U. S. Dept. of Commerce data

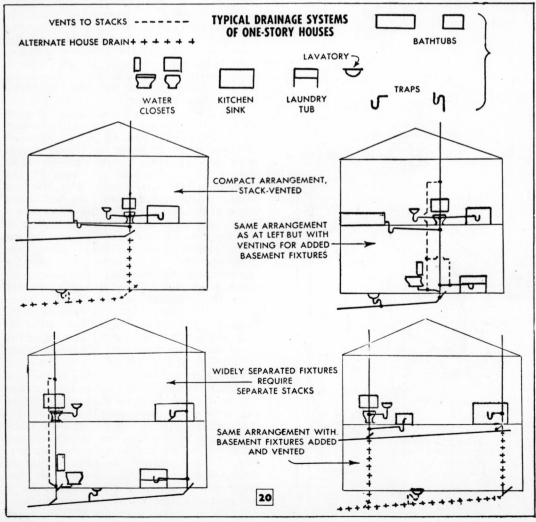

VENTS TO STACKS -------

ALTERNATE HOUSE DRAIN + + + + + +

TYPICAL DRAINAGE SYSTEMS OF ONE-STORY HOUSES

BATHTUBS

LAVATORY

WATER CLOSETS   KITCHEN SINK   LAUNDRY TUB

TRAPS

COMPACT ARRANGEMENT, STACK-VENTED

SAME ARRANGEMENT AS AT LEFT BUT WITH VENTING FOR ADDED BASEMENT FIXTURES

WIDELY SEPARATED FIXTURES REQUIRE SEPARATE STACKS

SAME ARRANGEMENT WITH BASEMENT FIXTURES ADDED AND VENTED

20

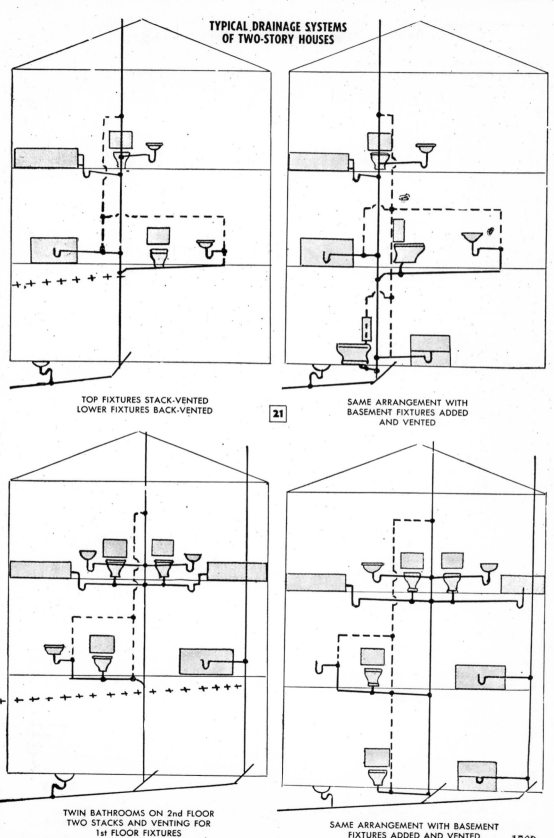

TYPICAL DRAINAGE SYSTEMS
OF TWO-STORY HOUSES

TOP FIXTURES STACK-VENTED
LOWER FIXTURES BACK-VENTED

21

SAME ARRANGEMENT WITH
BASEMENT FIXTURES ADDED
AND VENTED

TWIN BATHROOMS ON 2nd FLOOR
TWO STACKS AND VENTING FOR
1st FLOOR FIXTURES

SAME ARRANGEMENT WITH BASEMENT
FIXTURES ADDED AND VENTED

The diameter of vent piping, as well as its length, depends on the number and type of fixtures served and their fixture-unit rating. After determining the fixture-unit load, refer to Fig. 19. Locate the fixture-unit value, or the next higher value, in the second column from the left and opposite the size of the soil stack. Then get the maximum pipe lengths and diameters from the right-hand columns. For example, to find the proper size and length of vent pipe to serve the installation of bathroom fixtures, as shown in Fig. 10, totaling five fixture units, and assuming the soil stack is 3 in., you find that 30 ft. of 1½-in. pipe will serve for 10 fixture units.

As a guide to recommended arrangements of drain and vent pipes, typical drainage systems of one and two-story houses are shown in Figs. 20 and 21.

Where traps are needed: Traps are extremely important parts of a plumbing system as they prevent the entrance of sewer gas into the building without materially retarding the drainage flow through them. A trap forms a dip in the line, which retains enough water discharged through it to provide a seal. The depth of the seal, as measured from the top of the dip to the crown weir or overflow, Fig. 22A, should not be less than 2 in., nor more than 4 in. Traps having a maximum seal are known as deep-seal traps and should be used where the seal is not replenished frequently and may be lost by evaporation: for example, some floor drains.

Each plumbing fixture should be provided with a trap located as close to its discharge outlet as possible. The vertical distance from the crown weir to the outlet should not be over 24 in. One trap may serve a combination fixture such as a sink and laundry tub, if one compartment is not more than 6 in. deeper than the other and the waste outlets are not more than 30 in. apart. One trap also may serve three single-compartment laundry tubs, sinks or lavatories adjacent to each other and not more than 30 in. apart, if the trap is centrally located. For correct sizes of traps to use on various fixtures, refer to Fig. 4, table A. No fixture should be double-trapped, requiring the waste to pass through two traps in succession before it reaches the soil or waste stack, or the house drain. This does not apply to the insertion of a grease trap in the waste line from a kitchen sink if the pipe between the two traps is vented, nor to an arrangement of emptying wastes into a drain or sink. See detail C of Fig. 23.

Types of traps: The kind of traps mostly used for sinks and lavatories are the gooseneck or P-type traps, such as the one shown in detail A of Fig. 22. The cast-iron variety

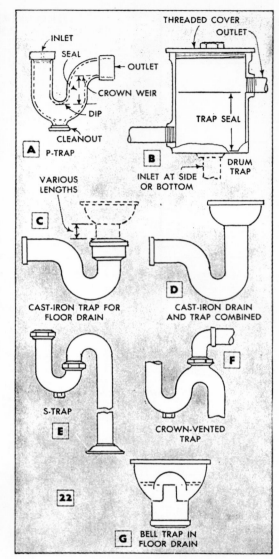

is installed on laundry tubs and basement sinks; the plated brass-tube kind is used where better appearance is desired. Some traps have cleanout plugs, others must be disconnected in case they become clogged. Those made of tubing have a slip joint at one end to fit on the discharge pipe of the fixture, and a union at the other end. Both joints are provided with washers.

Drum-type traps, detail B, are capable of discharging greater quantities of water, and are used mostly for bathtubs and shower stalls. They are set in the floor so that the cleanout cover is accessible, either from above or below. Traps of water closets are cast integrally with the bowl portion.

Detail C shows a cast-iron P-trap used for floor drains. Sometimes a drain and trap are combined in a single casting as shown in detail D. No venting is required for a

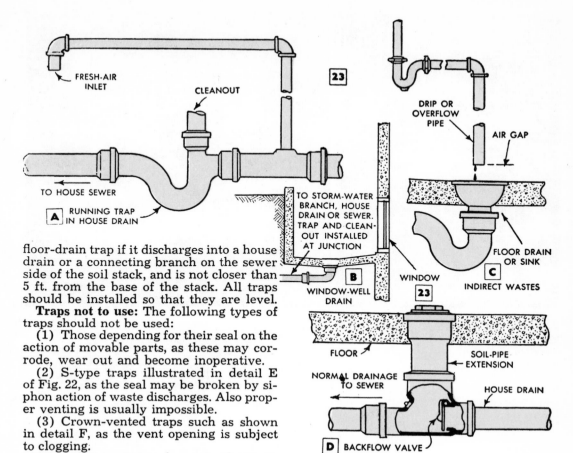

floor-drain trap if it discharges into a house drain or a connecting branch on the sewer side of the soil stack, and is not closer than 5 ft. from the base of the stack. All traps should be installed so that they are level.

Traps not to use: The following types of traps should not be used:

(1) Those depending for their seal on the action of movable parts, as these may corrode, wear out and become inoperative.

(2) S-type traps illustrated in detail E of Fig. 22, as the seal may be broken by siphon action of waste discharges. Also proper venting is usually impossible.

(3) Crown-vented traps such as shown in detail F, as the vent opening is subject to clogging.

(4) Bell-type traps shown in detail G, which are often used for floor drains; the seal depends on a partition which in time may be corroded or broken, thus destroying the ability of the trap to retain a seal.

House traps: Where required by local code, a "running" house trap is installed in the house drain near its outlet, as shown in Fig. 23A. Its function is to prevent sewer gases from getting into the plumbing system of the building, but it is objectionable from the standpoint that the trap reduces the discharge capacity of the drain and also causes back pressure. The fresh-air inlet or relief vent of a house trap need not be larger than half the size of the drain pipe to which it connects.

Storm-drain traps: Storm-water drains connected to combination house drains and sewers are trapped either by an individual trap in each branch or by a single trap in the main drain before it connects to the combination sewer. No traps are required for drains emptying into sewers used for storm water exclusively. Any underground trap, except a P-trap of a floor drain, should be provided with an accessible cleanout, and should be protected from frost.

Window-well and areaway drains: Often deep window wells or other areas such as

basement entrances are provided with drains, Fig. 23B. This is particularly true in locations where they are apt to fill up with snow. Since water in a trap at the drain would be subject to freezing, a trap and cleanout are provided underground in the line just before it connects to a storm-water branch, house drain or house sewer.

Refrigerator and other indirect wastes: Waste water dripping from an ice-cooled refrigerator, or the overflow of a water tank, can be discharged into a sink or floor drain as shown in Fig. 23C. An advantage of this arrangement is that it maintains a constant seal in the trap because of the continuous or occasional discharge. An air gap should be provided between the trap and the drip pipe. In case of a refrigerator, or any other device containing food, the drainpipe should be provided with a separate trap to prevent the passage of air and insects to the interior. In no case should the drainpipe of any food-containing device be connected directly to a drainage system.

Backflow valve in house drain: Where sewers are overtaxed and backflow into house-drainage systems is likely to occur, particularly in case of combination sewers after a heavy rainfall, it is advisable to in-

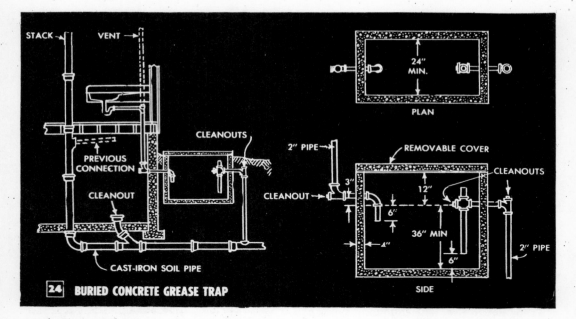

BURIED CONCRETE GREASE TRAP

stall a backflow valve in the house drain. The best location is just within the building near the outlet of the drain. If located within arm's reach under the basement floor, access is possible by simply extending the top opening with a length of soil pipe as shown in Fig. 23D. The hub is closed by means of a ferrule and brass screw plug. Where the distance from floor to backflow valve is more than 12 or 15 in., it is best to provide a concrete pit of convenient size.

Grease trap or catch basin: Some communities require a catch basin or grease trap. A grease trap should be used in an individual disposal system when grease drained into the kitchen sink is more than average. However, a grease trap should not be connected in the same waste line with a garbage-disposal unit. Grease traps may be of the small undersink variety, which require frequent cleaning, or the large kind buried outside of the house but as close as possible to the sink as in Fig. 24, which also gives recommended dimensions. The trap extends to ground level and a suitable cover is provided. As a rule grease traps are generally not required for small homes. Their use has been discontinued in many communities mostly because of the usual neglect in cleaning them.

Pipe cleanouts: Cleanout plugs are shown in Fig. 25A. One should be installed at the base of each soil or waste stack. One should also be installed near the junction of the house drain and house sewer, and at each change of direction of the house drain that is greater than 45 deg. Cleanouts are quite necessary at the upstream end of long horizontal waste lines, Fig. 25B, especially those from kitchen sinks, where congealed

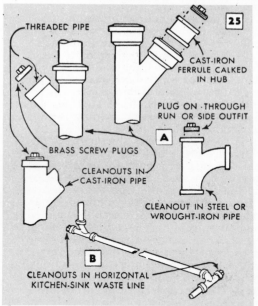

grease in the pipe may cause clogging. In homes built on cement slabs or over crawl spaces less than 18 in. high, the stack-base cleanout can be projected just outside of the building wall downstream from the stack. When a cleanout is used in an underground drain, it should be made accessible by extending it to or above grade level, and directly over its location. Similarly, cleanouts for concealed piping in walls and floors should be accessible.

Installing drainage system in existing house: Installation of a drainage system starts with placing the stack base or foot piece; then laying the house drain and set-

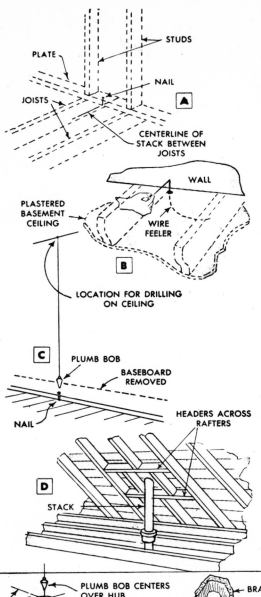

STUDS

PLATE

NAIL

JOISTS

A

CENTERLINE OF
STACK BETWEEN
JOISTS

WALL

PLASTERED
BASEMENT
CEILING

WIRE
FEELER

B

LOCATION FOR DRILLING
ON CEILING

C PLUMB BOB

BASEBOARD
REMOVED

NAIL

HEADERS ACROSS
RAFTERS

D

STACK

ting up the stack. First make a few preliminary checks to see if the stack and fixtures can be installed as planned. Also recheck the location of the waste and vent pipes through partitions and floors to the points where they connect to the soil stack. If the stack is to run inside a wide partition, remove the baseboard at the first-floor level, and drive a 10d finishing nail through the floor next to the partition to indicate the stack centerline. Fig. 26A. Then check the nail position from the basement to see whether stack will come between joists. If necessary alter the stack centerline for clearance. If the basement ceiling is plastered, get a ¼ by 18-in. electrician's bit and ratchet brace, and drill through the floor next to the plate. A bent wire should be used to feel where the joists are located, as in detail B.

Next, suspend a plumb bob from the ceiling of the first floor directly above the nail or hole, in detail C, and mark the ceiling. Then tap on a block held against the ceiling to check the position of joists. If the distance from mark to joist is insufficient for stack clearance, make the necessary adjustment both at this point and also below. If this is impossible, plan to use a header so the joist can be cut to provide clearance. When the center of stack location through the ceiling is decided, drill a hole through the ceiling and floor above it as a basis for further lineup to the second-floor ceiling. If the stack position comes directly under a rafter, plan either to install headers as in detail D or to offset the stack.

Laying the house drain: Drop a plumb line from the center of the stack position at the basement ceiling to mark the basement floor. Next, mark a line on the floor from this point toward the point where the house drain is to connect to the house sewer. Similarly mark locations of the branch drains.

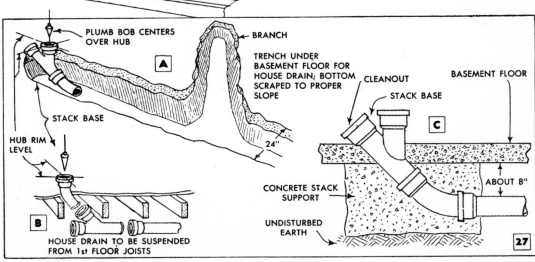

PLUMB BOB CENTERS
OVER HUB

BRANCH

A

TRENCH UNDER
BASEMENT FLOOR FOR
HOUSE DRAIN; BOTTOM
SCRAPED TO PROPER
SLOPE

CLEANOUT

STACK BASE

BASEMENT FLOOR

C

STACK BASE

HUB RIM
LEVEL

24"

CONCRETE STACK
SUPPORT

ABOUT 8"

B

HOUSE DRAIN TO BE SUSPENDED
FROM 1st FLOOR JOISTS

UNDISTURBED
EARTH

27

Break up a strip of floor about 24 in. wide, centering at the marked lines, and dig trenches as in Fig. 27A. The 24-in. width gives just enough space to calk the pipe joints. Start digging at the stack location, just deep enough for cast-iron soil pipe to rest about 8 in. below the floor. Continue the trench toward the outlet, increasing its depth as necessary to obtain the proper slope, which can be ascertained by the method shown in Fig. 33A.

The stack base may consist of a 45-deg. Y-fitting and a ⅛ bend fitted together and calked, or it may be a specially made stack base. Both are shown in Fig. 12. If the house drain is to be suspended from the basement ceiling, the fittings are arranged as shown in Fig. 27B, and the line is supported with hangers spaced not over 5 ft. apart. In either case, the stack base is adjusted so that the hub to which the stack is to connect is perfectly level across its rim and also centers around the suspended plumb bob. Tamp earth firmly around the pipe to hold it in position temporarily. Then continue to install sections of pipe in the trench. The hubs always point upstream. The proper fittings are installed at the right points to connect branch lines, using long-sweep fittings with the branch inlets pointing downstream. No double-hub nor double-T fitting should be used in horizontal soil or waste lines. To locate the fittings correctly, you may have to cut lengths of pipe. The hub and spigot ends of adjoining pipes must be concentric so that the annular space for calking is of uniform width. The trench bottom should support the entire barrel portions of the pipe; therefore slight concavities are dug under the hubs as shown in Fig. 33B.

The trench is not filled with earth until the drainage system has been tested for leaks. This will be explained in detail later. When laying a house drain it is sometimes more convenient to start laying the pipe from the outlet toward the stack. When this procedure is followed the stack-base assembly must be shifted about 2½ in. so that the last joint can be made, after which it is forced back to its original position, adjusting the hub to get it level. When the house drain has been completed, dig a space under the stack base about 18 to 24 in. square and about 10 in. deep. Fill this with concrete as shown in Fig. 27C for good stack support.

Setting up the stack: After the concrete has set for a day or so you can begin to assemble the stack. If a waste connection from the laundry tub goes to the stack, install a T-fitting and calk the joint, making sure that it is plumb. Where basement waste pipes are not so connected you install a full 5-ft. length of soil pipe. Then cut holes in the first floor, one through the partition sill or next to it, depending on the

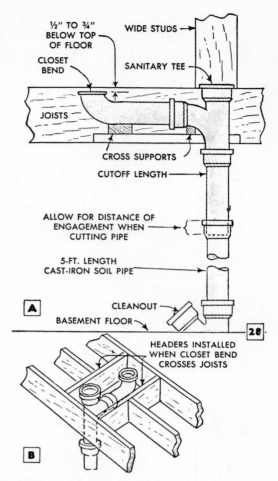

exact stack location. Another hole should be cut for the outlet of the water-closet bend, if a water closet is planned for the first floor. It usually is necessary to open the floor to install pipes, although an open basement ceiling often permits installing pipes from below.

The second pipe length must be cut short so that the sanitary T-fitting for the water-closet connection will be at the right height as shown in Fig. 28A. The closet bend or pipe extension to it is arranged at the proper slope so that the outlet of the bend comes ½ to ¾ in. below the top of the floor. If the bend is too long it can be cut. One or more supporting crosspieces on cleats nailed to joists are used to support horizontal soil pipe between joists. Where a closet bend or extension crosses joists, headers are provided as shown in Fig. 28B. The stack also must be supported at least every 8 ft., as described on p. 1729. It will be necessary to remove a strip of plaster from floor to ceiling, Fig. 32A, when soil pipe is set in a partition. You may have to "box out" the wall to accommodate the pipe.

After the stack has been completed to

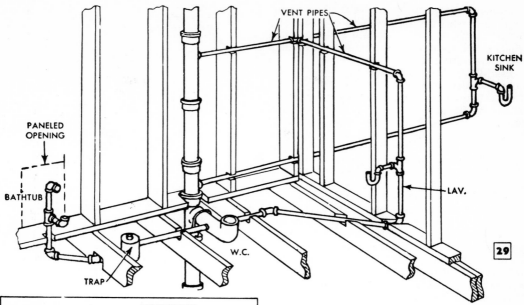

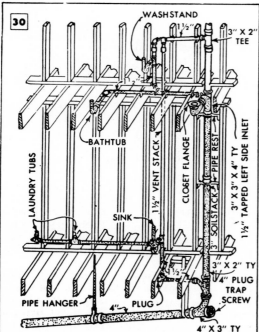

SUPPORTING AND ROUGHING-IN A SIMPLE SYSTEM
HAVING CONTINUOUS WASTES AND VENTS.
DRAINAGE PIPES ARE STIPPLED AND VENT PIPES ARE
OUTLINED

Above this point the fittings for waste and vent connections are incorporated, and the stack is continued so that it will extend no less than 6 in. above the roof, shingles having been removed and the roof boards already cut. Stack flashing is installed when the shingles are replaced. Openings in floors and partitions where pipes are installed should be ratproofed with sheet metal.

Concealed waste and vent pipes: Concealed work in new-house construction is comparatively simple but in existing homes some flooring must be taken up and plaster removed. To cross joists and studs, notches are cut in them, as shown in Figs. 29 and 30. Where joists or studs are weakened by notching, they should be reinforced. To connect drainage and water-supply pipes to a built-in tub, accessibility is provided by opening the wall, framing the opening and then providing a door or panel, as in Fig. 31. A bathtub trap must be accessible. Drum traps are the most adaptable for underfloor work, being arranged so that the cover is flush with the floor or is accessible from below.

Opening walls and floors: Fig. 32A shows how a minimum amount of wall covering is removed to install waste and vent pipes. After marking off the exact location of the pipes on the walls, cut through plaster and plaster base as required. Vertical cuts through plaster are made alongside studs, and cleats are nailed to the studs for fastening the wire lath, as shown in detail B. In small bathrooms flooring may have to be removed entirely from wall to wall to uncover an area large enough to install the pipes. If cutting a floor is necessary, use a

the first-floor level, check the exact location of connections to waste pipes, select fittings accordingly and cut the pipe where necessary. In case no water closet is planned for the lower floor, a connection may be required for the waste line from the kitchen sink, although this may also be brought to the stack underneath the floor. Continue building up the stack to the water-closet extension on the second floor.

keyhole saw, starting to cut from a small hole and sawing alongside the joists. See detail C. This permits nailing a cleat to the joists as a base to which the cut floor boards are later nailed.

Installing house sewer: Although the house sewer may be installed before the house-drainage system, it is often done afterwards. Its size should not be less than that of the house drain, and it may have to be larger, as for instance when storm water is emptied into it. It is important that the joints be made watertight and rootproof. The line should be as straight as possible and should be below the frost depth. The usual slope is ¼ in. per ft., and the method of determining the slope is shown in Fig. 33A. Various kinds of pipe are used for house sewers as described in the section on pipe. An acid-resisting type of pipe is needed when the soil contains cinders and ashes as metal pipe then is subject to excessive corrosion. When some types of pipe other than cast-iron pipe are laid in filled or unstable soil, they should be placed on concrete pads for uniform support.

Digging trenches: Digging a trench in clay or other compact earth usually is safe, but in unstable soil, particularly sand, it is necessary to prevent the sides from caving in. "Shoring" for sides to prevent cave-ins consists of planks—or forms rented from a concrete contractor—which are suitably braced as shown in Fig. 33C. The pipe should be placed on compact, undisturbed earth. Rocks at the trench bottom should be removed. If the bottom is very rocky excavate 4 in. below grade and backfill with fine gravel or coarse sand to assure uniform support of the pipe.

In case the drop from the house-drain outlet to the city sewer or individual septic tank is much greater than can be negotiated with pipe slope, an additional drop may be required. This can be provided by a short steep slope near the city sewer as in Fig. 33D. The drop can be located also at the house-end of the line as in detail E. A drop that slopes more than 45 deg. from the horizontal should be provided with a cleanout opening. In no case should a drop be located within 15 ft. from the entrance to a septic tank, since the accelerated velocity of the drainage flow would interfere with the proper action of the tank. A T-fitting inserted at the outlet end of the house sewer, detail D, provides a means of sealing this end of the line when making a leak test on the drainage system after it is completed.

Connection to city sewer: Connection to the city sewer usually is done by or under supervision of municipal employees. Vitrified-clay sewers generally are provided with 6-in. Y-fittings at each lot location for attachment of house sewers, requiring only

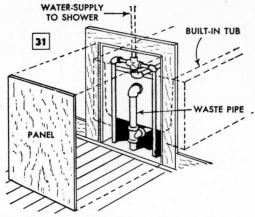

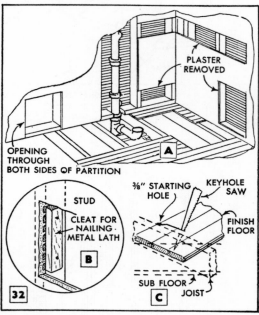

the removal of the plug and the insertion of a curved section of pipe. Concrete sewers generally must be tapped and a pipe stub cemented in the hole. The trench in which the house sewer is laid is not filled until after testing has been accomplished. When filling a trench containing a pipe that can be damaged, such as vitrified-clay pipe, avoid throwing large stones and rocks in with the fill until the pipe has been covered for a depth of at least a foot or so. Thus you avoid unnecessary breakage.

Testing for leaks: After a drainage system has been completed, it should be tested for leaks before the installation is approved. To make the test, close the street end of the house sewer with a test plug or do it by plugging the pipe with a bag of wet clay as in Fig. 33F. Close all other openings below the stack terminal. On waste pipes you simply use pipe caps. Closet-bent and floor-

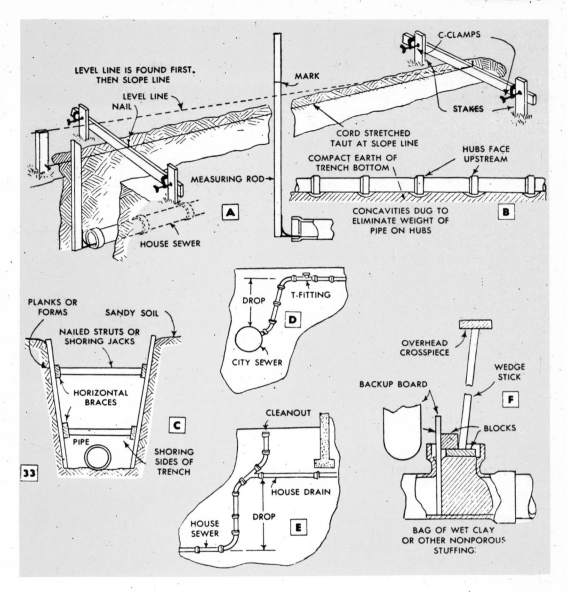

drain openings can be closed with test plugs or bags of clay.

When all openings are made leakproof, fill the system with water through the stack terminal, using a hose. Then inspect all the joints and pipes for leakage. If leaks are found at joints, the cause usually is defective calking, although a pipe may be defective also. Such joints are recalked or defective pipe replaced after letting out the water by opening the house sewer. The surfaces to be calked should be thoroughly dry. After the final test, the T-fitting in the house sewer is closed by cementing in a disk.

Frost protection and insulation: Besides the need of burying the house sewer at a depth sufficient to prevent freezing, soil and waste pipes installed in outside walls or in unheated spaces under floors often require insulation against freezing. Insulation is applied all around the pipe, especially between them and the outside walls. Cold drafts in partitions and floors may be stopped by headers nailed across the studs or joists. Sometimes warm air admitted through a register from the basement is highly effective in preventing frozen waste pipes. Noise caused by water being discharged through soil and waste pipes is sometimes objectionable. It may be amplified considerably if the pipe is in contact with a wall. Where such effects can be anticipated, the pipes should be wrapped with soundproofing insulation when they are installed.

PIPE FOR ANY PLUMBING JOB

IT MAKES A BIG DIFFERENCE, generally, what kind of pipe and fittings you use for a plumbing job. Some kinds are developed for specific purposes while others have a variety of uses or may be more suitable for some jobs than others, besides varying in cost and durability. Therefore the reference data contained in this section concerning various kinds of pipe and fittings, their purposes, and also how pipe is prepared and installed will be of help in selecting and using pipe.

Kinds of pipe for plumbing: Pipe can be classified as to its use in home plumbing systems as follows: (1) Water-supply pipe, which may be galvanized wrought-iron and steel pipe, brass and copper pipe, copper tubing and also plastic pipe; (2) drain and vent pipe, which may be galvanized wrought-iron and steel pipe, cast-iron soil pipe, vitrified clay pipe, cement pipe, lead pipe, copper pipe and tubing, asbestos-cement pipe and bituminized-fiber pipe. Some of these are used for different purposes; others are restricted to certain specific applications and treatment.

Wrought-iron and steel pipe: Used for water distribution, for waste and vent lines, wrought-iron pipe is more resistant

to rust than steel pipe but also is more expensive. Either kind is available in black or galvanized finish, but only the latter should be used for permanently installed lines because of the added protection it provides against rust. Life of galvanized steel pipe generally ranges from 15 to 30 years; that of wrought-iron pipe from 20 to 40 years. Identifying wrought-iron and steel pipe from appearance is difficult for the average person, and therefore he must rely for this on the manufacturer's markings put on first-grade pipe of either type. Reference here to steel pipe also includes steel-alloy pipe, such as copper-bearing pipe which contains about 0.2 percent of copper by weight and usually is galvanized.

Standard-weight wrought-iron or steel pipe comes in random lengths up to 22 ft., with both ends threaded and protected with couplings. Sizes range from 1/8 to 12-in. nominal inside diameters. Fig. 1 gives dimensions and other data on wrought-iron and steel pipe up to 2½-in. size. Besides the standard weight there is also an "extra strong" and a "double extra strong" weight. These, having thicker walls than standard-weight pipe, are used for higher pressures than usually found in most home plumbing

DATA ON STANDARD WEIGHT WROUGHT IRON AND STEEL PIPE FROM ⅛″ TO 2½″; FURNISHED IN RANDOM LENGTHS UP TO 22 FT. (All Dimensions in Inches)						
Nominal Size	Outside Diameter	Inside Diameter	Wall Thickness	No. of Threads Per In.	Length of Effective Threads	Normal Engagement For Tight Fit (W)
⅛	0.405	0.269	0.068	27	.2639	¼
¼	0.540	0.364	.088	18	.4018	5/16
⅜	0.675	0.493	0.091	18	.4078	⅜
½	0.840	0.622	0.109	14	.5337	7/16
¾	1.050	0.824	0.113	14	.5457	½
1	1.315	1.049	0.133	11½	.6828	9/16
1¼	1.660	1.380	0.140	11½	.7068	9/16
1½	1.900	1.610	0.145	11½	.7235	9/16
2	2.375	2.067	0.154	11½	.7565	⅝
2½	2.875	2.469	0.203	8	1.1375	⅞

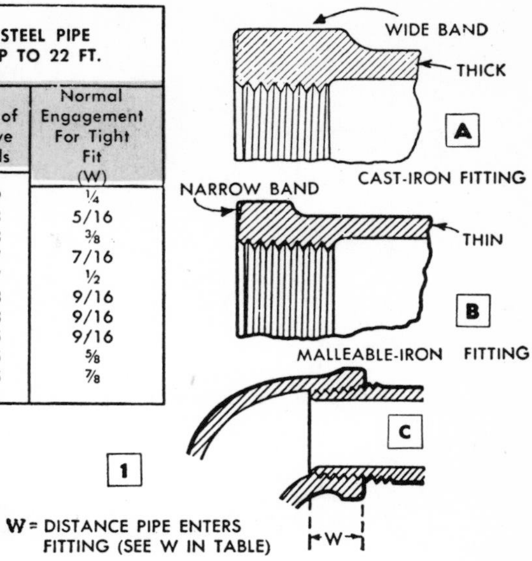

1

W = DISTANCE PIPE ENTERS FITTING (SEE W IN TABLE)

systems. The outside diameters of pipes having different wall thicknesses are the same, but the inside diameters vary. For example, the outside diameter of a 1-in. standard-weight pipe and that of a 1-in. double-extra-strong pipe are both 1.315 in., but the inside diameter of the former is 1.049 in., and that of the latter is only .599 in.

Water-pipe fittings: The only pipe fittings that are made of wrought iron and steel are nipples and couplings. Both are short lengths of pipe, nipples being threaded externally and couplings internally. Other fittings are made of cast iron or malleable iron. Malleable iron is preferable as it is tougher and not so brittle as cast iron. You can distinguish between cast-iron and malleable-iron fittings in that the latter have thinner and narrower bands as shown in Fig. 1A and B. Fittings in water lines should be galvanized to retard rusting.

A number of fittings in common use are shown in Fig. 3. Externally threaded ends are called "male" ends and internally threaded ends are referred to as "female." Nipples come in various lengths—17 lengths from 1⅜ to 12 in. in the ¾-in. size. Couplings connect two pipes end to end where they need not be disconnected later. A reducing coupling joins pipes of different sizes. Unions connect pipes end to end near meters, water heaters and other fixtures that may have to be disconnected; unions also are placed in a line where a branch line may be inserted later. Flange-type unions generally are used on pipes over 2 in. in size.

Regular and reducing elbows join pipe at 45 and 90 deg.; street elbows (45 and 90 deg.) differ in that they have one tapped and one threaded end, the latter end to join another pipe fitting or a matching tapped hole. Regular or reducing tees join three pipes at 90 deg.; a street tee has one outlet threaded like a street elbow. A Y-branch connects two pipes end to end, and a third pipe at a 45 deg. angle. There are also regular and reducing crosses.

Plugs are used to close one end of a fitting; caps to close the end of pipe. Bushings have a hexagon bearing surface to take a wrench; they are threaded internally and externally to make a connection from a pipe or fitting of one size to one of another size, where a reducing coupling cannot be used. Return bends connect the ends of two or more pipes running parallel to each other, as in a bank of pipes used for heating. Return bends are furnished in close, medium and open types for different spacing of pipes. On ¾-in. pipe, return bends have 1½, 1⅞ and 2½-in. center-to-center spacing respectively. Hose fittings have different threads and will not fit standard threaded pipe and fittings, except sill cocks and laundry faucets, which are threaded to permit hose connections.

Fittings for threaded drainage pipes: Fittings for threaded drainage pipes differ radically in design from ordinary pipe fittings. Those of larger sizes are usually cast iron. One essential difference between regular and drainage fittings is shown in Fig. 4. The internal diameter of the body section of a drainage fitting is the same as that of the pipe it fits. The tapped section of the fitting is recessed so that the end of the pipe butts against the shoulder, thus preventing a "ledge" against which waste can collect and start an obstruction. The second essential difference between regular and drainage fittings is that the latter have slightly slanted or pitched outlets (¼ in. per ft.) for connection to horizontal drainage and vent pipes that must be pitched. In Fig. 5, which shows a number of common drainage fittings. Pitch is indicated by the dotted lines. In drainage lines, fittings of long radii or a combination of fittings for gradual change of direction should be used

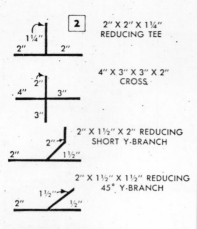

2	2" X 2" X 1¼" REDUCING TEE
	4" X 3" X 3" X 2" CROSS
	2" X 1½" X 2" REDUCING SHORT Y-BRANCH
	2" X 1½" X 1½" REDUCING 45° Y-BRANCH

HOW TO SPECIFY SIZES OF REDUCING FITTINGS

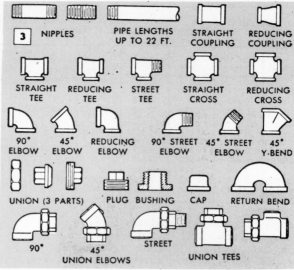

wherever possible as a preventive measure against stoppage.

Ordering pipe fittings: All fittings are referred to by the pipe size on which they are used, which precedes the name of the fitting. For example, a ¾-in. elbow has both outlets for ¾-in. pipe. In giving the sizes of reducing tees and Y-branches, the larger run is given first, then the smaller run followed by the inlet or branch, as indicated in Fig. 2. Reducing crosses should be specified similarly except that both outlets are given, the smaller one last. For crosses having both run openings of the same size and both outlets of one size, only the run and outlet sizes need be given. For bushings the external size comes first, then the internal size.

Brass and copper pipe: While the initial cost of brass and copper pipe is more than that of wrought-iron and steel pipe, it will last the life of a building. It is required in some localities where water is extremely corrosive. Besides the economy gained by avoiding replacement of steel pipe, of which a large percentage is labor cost, it is possible to use smaller sizes of brass and copper pipes, which means a saving. Smaller sizes can be used since brass and copper pipe has a smooth inside surface which causes less resistance to the flow of water than iron and steel pipe of similar size.

Brass and copper pipe is furnished in the same sizes and in practically the same wall thicknesses as iron and steel pipe, but in 12-ft. lengths. Threads are also the same size except for the fine thread used on thin-wall drainage fittings. When cutting and threading brass and copper pipe, a lubricant or cooling medium such as lard oil or soapy water reduces effort and helps to produce clean, sharp threads. Wrenches of

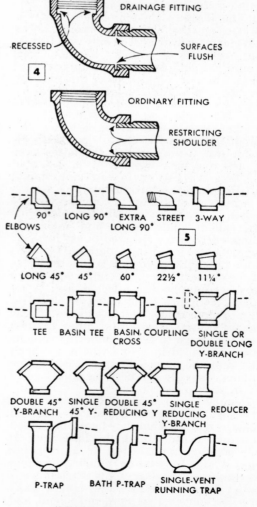

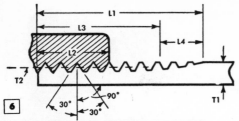

6

L1 — TOTAL APPROXIMATE THREAD LENGTH ON PIPE
L2 — NORMAL ENGAGEMENT OF FITTING BY HAND
L3 — EFFECTIVE THREADS THAT SHOULD BE SCREWED INTO FITTING
L4 — THREE TO FOUR IMPERFECT THREADS DUE TO DIE
T1 — FULL WALL THICKNESS OF PIPE
T2 — TAPER OF ¾ IN. PER FT. ON DIAMETER

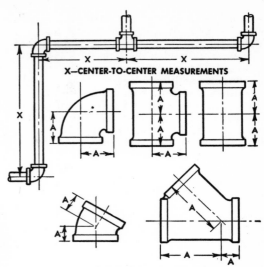

X—CENTER-TO-CENTER MEASUREMENTS

A—CENTER-TO-FACE DIMENSIONS

7

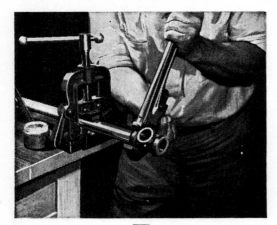

8

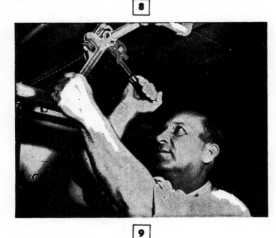

9

the friction or strap type should be used to avoid marring brass and copper wire. Also, the vises should be fitted with friction clamps instead of toothed jaws.

For brass pipe, the fittings used are the same type as those for iron and steel pipe. Special alloy fittings for either brass or copper pipe are used. Iron or steel fittings should not be used on brass and copper pipe as they will rust faster because of electrolytic action between dissimilar metals. Chrome-plated brass pipe generally is used for exposed portions of water-supply and drainage lines that run from floors or walls to fixtures.

Standard pipe threads: To assure strong, well-fitting joints that are watertight, threads on pipe must be of correct length and depth and must be clean and sharp. Pipe threads have a taper of ¾ in. per foot. Fig. 6 shows the number of threads required on pipe for a good fit. Such correct thread length results when the die is brought flush with the end of the pipe or when the pipe projects only half a turn beyond the die. Table, Fig. 1, gives the correct distance that the threaded end of pipe should enter fittings as indicated in detail C.

How to measure pipe runs: When installing pipe, first take the actual center-to-center measurements of the pipe run, as indicated by letter X in Fig. 7. The lengths of pipe between the various fittings must be shorter than the X-dimensions to allow space for the fittings, yet must be greater than the distance between the fittings to allow for the portions of pipe entering them. Therefore you first subtract dimension A of the fittings from the X-dimensions, but then add the distances that the pipe enters the fittings as given in Table Fig. 1.

Making threaded pipe joints: Before screwing pipe into a fitting or vice versa, use a stiff bristle or wire brush to clean chips and dirt from the threads of each. Next, smear some pipe-thread compound or "dope" over the threads of the pipe only, but not on the inside threads of a fitting as this causes it to collect on the end of the pipe and to restrict pipe diameter at this point, besides imparting a disagreeable taste to water. Such a restriction interferes with the flow of water; also this forms a "drag" for building up a lime deposit that may eventually clog the pipe. Theoretically a watertight joint results from good threading and assembling, but there are slight variations that may result from threading, or there may be variations in the threads of fittings which can cause leakage at joints even though they appear tight. Therefore, it is general practice to use pipe-thread compound at all joints.

Defective fittings that are not tapped deep enough should not be used. Cutting a deeper thread on the pipe with an adjustable die in order to compensate for this only weakens the pipe by reducing its wall thickness, which may cause it to break later. It's better to replace the pipe, fitting or both. If threads fit properly a pipe can be screwed into a fitting, or vice versa, a distance of three or four threads by hand. A pipe wrench then is used to draw it up snugly. Often it is possible to attach or detach a fitting while the pipe is held in a vise as in Fig. 8. Generally, two wrenches are needed for assembling pipe, one on the pipe and the other on the fitting as illustrated in Fig. 9. Moderate pressure on wrenches should be sufficient. Excessive pressure may distort the fitting or squash the pipe. Exposed threads of iron or steel pipe joints should be coated with a suitable rust-resisting paint such as red lead or asphalt roofing paint.

Plastic pipe: Comparatively new but rapidly being accepted for many applications, strong, durable plastic pipe offers some specific advantages. It is extremely lightweight, from ⅛ to 1/13 the weight of metal pipe as evident from Fig. 10. It is rust, rot and corrosion proof; it can be cut with a saw or knife. Some kinds are especially designed to convey liquids intended for human consumption. Plastic pipe is entirely practical for jet wells and other cold-water plumbing installations, but it should not be used for hot-water lines or subjected to excessive heat.

The pipe comes in three forms — rigid, semirigid and flexible. Both the flexible and rigid kinds are shown in Fig. 11. The flexible pipe is ideal for installation in trenches as in Fig. 12. Available sizes range from ½ to 6-in. nominal inside diameters. The rigid pipe comes in 20-ft. lengths and is useful for well casings, septic-tank lines, field drainage, sprinkler and irrigation installations. The flexible pipe comes in coils from 100 to 400 ft. in length. It is especially suitable for jet wells and water-supply and distribution lines in locations free from rodent attack. Low temperature does not damage the pipe as it expands with freezing water.

Numerous fittings are available for both

Yardley Plastics Co. photos

types so that any kind of connection can be made. Varying with the composition of the pipe, connections are made by insert couplings and clamps and insert adapters. Connections are also made by cementing the pipe into a fitting, which within a few minutes results in a joint as strong as the pipe itself. You can use compression fittings and also threaded joints. Threaded joints are practical for low-pressure or gravity lines but not recommended for vertical runs. In threading the pipe, it is recommended that a mandrel be inserted for support. The same threading equipment as for standard metal pipe is used. Plain or soapy water is used as a cutting solution—not oil or lead. The threaded pipe is assembled with strap wrenches; pipe wrenches will damage the pipe. No pipe-joint compound is required at the threaded joint.

Copper tubing: Copper tubing has thinner walls than copper pipe and costs less yet is sufficiently strong to withstand all pressures normally encountered in water-supply lines and thus offers practically the same advantages for home plumbing. Copper tubing is also easy to install and it can be run through closed partitions, Fig. 13, when replacing rusted-out iron or steel pipe, or when installing plumbing in a house not previously piped.

Copper tubing is furnished in three wall thicknesses (types K, L and M) for assembly with either solder or compression-type fittings. Type K is the heaviest and most durable. Type L has a slightly thinner wall. Both are furnished either hard in 20-ft. straight lengths, or soft in 60 and 100-ft. coils. Type M is still thinner than the other types of tubing of the same size. It is furnished only hard in 1¼ to 12-in. sizes and only in 20-ft. straight lengths, and is generally installed with soldered fittings, not being intended for use with compres-

Copper & Brass Research Assn. photo

13

Anaconda photo

14

DIMENSIONS OF K, L AND M-TYPES COPPER TUBING FROM ⅜″ TO 2″

Nominal Size	Outside Diameter	Inside Diameter				Wall Thickness		
	Types K-L-M	Type K	Type L	Type M	Type K	Type L	Type M
⅜	.500	.402	.430		.049	.035	
½	.625	.527	.545		.049	.040	
⅝	.750	.652	.666		.049	.042	
¾	.875	.745	.785		.065	.045	
1	1.125	.995	1.025		.065	.050	
1¼	1.375	1245	1265	1291	.065	.055	.042
1½	1.625	1481	1505	1527	.072	.060	.049
2	2.125	1959	1985	2009	.083	.070	.058

(All Dimensions in Inches)

15

TYPES OF COMPRESSION FITTINGS

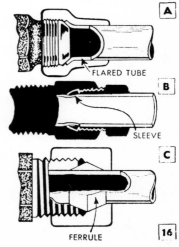

A

FLARED TUBE

B

SLEEVE

C

FERRULE

16

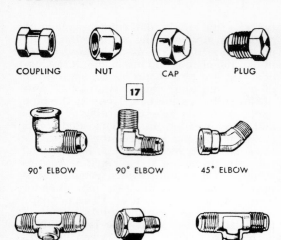

COUPLING NUT CAP PLUG

17

90° ELBOW 90° ELBOW 45° ELBOW

REDUCING TEE REDUCER TEE

18

19

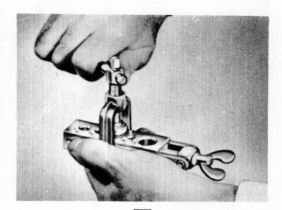

20

21

sion fittings. Dimensions of copper tubing, of sizes from ⅜ to 2 in., are given in Fig. 15. In home plumbing, the hard variety is preferred for horizontal lines; soft tubing is difficult to install without sag between supports, which prevents good drainage of the system. Soft tubing is satisfactory for vertical risers.

For underground water service, as in Fig. 14, soft tubing of type-K thickness is recommended. Compression-type fittings are better suited mechanically to resist the settling movement of earth. The fittings should be tack-soldered for added security. The tubing should not be laid directly on stones or rock, and when filling the trench, a 12-in. layer of soft dirt is thrown over the tubing before adding stones for fill. Where copper tubing is embedded in cinders, it should be protected from the acid that is formed, This is accomplished by means of a layer of sand mixed with lime that extends well above and below the pipe.

Compression fittings: Fig. 16 shows three kinds of compression fittings for connecting copper tubing. The kind in detail A requires flaring the tube ends. The kind shown in detail B is assembled by merely pushing the tube into the fitting and then tightening the nut. This shears the sleeve from the nut and also compresses it tightly on the tube to which it then becomes permanently attached. Detail C shows a somewhat similar compression fitting in which a ferrule is also compressed on the tube. The ferrule has two tapers, one seating in the nut and the other in the body of the fitting. Fig. 17 shows a number of generally used fittings of the flared-tube type. The process of connecting tubes to them consists of cutting a tube off squarely, Fig. 18, and reaming off the burr inside and out, with a reamer or round file, Fig. 19. You then flare the end of the tubing after a sleeve nut has been slipped on, Fig. 20. The final assembly is

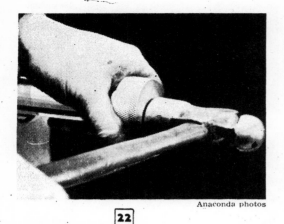

22

Anaconda photos

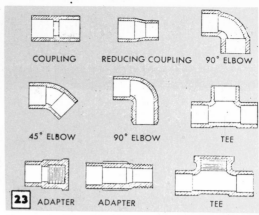

23

COUPLING   REDUCING COUPLING   90° ELBOW

45° ELBOW   90° ELBOW   TEE

ADAPTER   ADAPTER   TEE

24

shown in Fig. 21. The tool section contains data on using these tools. Flaring can also be done with a punch and hammer as in Fig. 22, particularly on tubing of larger sizes.

Solder-type fittings: Fig. 23 shows some solder-type fittings; a large variety of others are furnished also. To install them, the ends of the tubing are first cut off squarely, either with a tube cutter or with a hacksaw as in Fig. 24. Then the cut ends are reamed to remove the burr. Often a sizing tool also is used to correct any possible distortion of the tube caused by handling—

Next, the surfaces to be soldered together must be thoroughly cleaned, using emery cloth or steel wool, as demonstrated in Fig. 25, until the metal is bright. All traces of discoloration must be removed to assure uniform adhesion of solder. Wipe off all particles of dust and steel wool with a clean rag or brush, after which you apply a thin film of soldering flux completely covering both surfaces, Fig. 26. Paste flux is usually easier to handle for this purpose than liquid flux. Push the fitting over the tube as far as it will go and turn it back and forth a few times to assure getting the flux over the surfaces evenly.

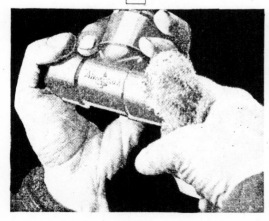

25

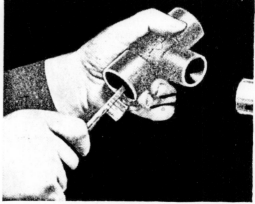

26

Anaconda photos

Heating comes next, using a blowtorch as shown in Fig. 27, or other type of torch. Direct the flame to all sides of the fitting if possible. While heating, touch the end of a length of wire solder to the edge of the fitting occasionally (outside the flame) to check for temperature. As soon as the solder liquefies instantly when touched to the fitting, the correct soldering temperature has been reached. Without waiting, feed solder between the tube and fitting by applying it all around the edge of the fitting, Fig. 28. The torch flame can be held on the fitting while solder is being applied to keep it hot. Generally the right amount of 1/8-in. solid-wire solder required is a length equal to the diameter of the tube. Kink the solder this distance from its end, and feed it up to this point. Solder applied at the edge of a fitting is drawn up between the contacting surfaces by capillary attraction, no matter at which angle the fitting is held. Solder even creeps up vertically this way for a greater distance than is required for making a good joint.

When applying solder, take care not to get it all over the tube or fitting. While solder is still liquid, you can use a rag or brush to wipe off any surplus, but leave it in the chamfer at the end of the fitting. Avoid movement of tube or fitting while the solder hardens; a disturbance at this time often causes weak joints. If the torch must be held near wood or other combustible material, protect the latter with a sheet of asbestos paper or asbestos board. An air-acetylene or liquefied-petroleum torch often is safer in such cases than a blowtorch as the flame is smaller.

To solder tubing into one or more outlets of a fitting already having a soldered joint, the solder in the existing joint is kept from melting by wrapping a wet rag around that portion of the fitting. Also, to disconnect a tube from a fitting without disturbing other soldered joints, use wet rags in the same way, as shown in Fig. 29. Large fittings require more care than small ones to heat them uniformly all around. This is particularly true with fittings of 2½ in. ir diameter and larger, such as copper vent waste tubes and soil tubes.

Kind of solder to use: A "soft" solder consisting of 95 percent tin and 5 percent antimony makes a considerably stronger joint than a 50-50 lead-and-tin solder. The former flows at temperatures in excess of 465 deg. F., and hardens at 450 deg., giving a plastic range of only 15 deg., which means quick hardening. This is desirable as it minimizes chances of poor adhesion caused by joint disturbance. Ordinary 50-50 lead-tin solder, customarily used by tinsmiths, melts at 250 deg. F., and has a 60-deg. plastic range. The best kind of solder for strong,

27

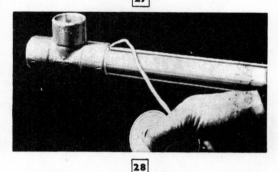

28

Anaconda photos

29

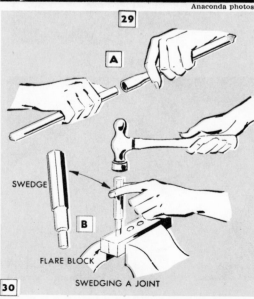

A

SWEDGE

B

FLARE BLOCK

SWEDGING A JOINT

30

Lead Industries Assn. photos

31

32

33 LEAD PIPE FOR VENT AND DRAINAGE LINES

I.D. (In.)	Wall Thickness (In.)		
1¼	118	139	171
1½	.138	.165	.191
2	.142	177	205
2½, 3, 4, 5, 6	.125		250

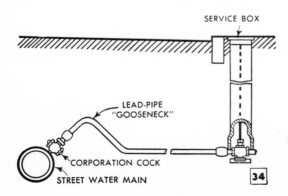

SERVICE BOX

LEAD-PIPE "GOOSENECK"

CORPORATION COCK

STREET WATER MAIN

34

durable joints at fittings is "hard" solder consisting of copper and phosphorus, sometimes with silver added, which flows at temperatures from 1300 to 1400 deg. F.

Bending copper tubes: It is often necessary to bend tubing to pass ordinary obstructions in building construction. Soft tubing is generally used for this. Use a bending spring to prevent kinks. Hard tubing requires annealing (softening) the portions to be bent. This can be done by heating the portion of tubing to a dull red with a blowtorch. Applying cold, soaked rags to the heated portion helps annealing and cools the metal quickly.

Swedged copper-tube joints: Two lengths of soft copper tubing (or hard tubing annealed at the ends) of equal diameter can be joined by swedging instead of using a coupling. The end of one length is expanded to fit over the end of the other as in Fig. 30A. Then they are sweat-soldered together. To make such a joint the ends are first cut off squarely and reamed to remove burr. Then a swedging tool of proper size is driven into the end of one length while held in a flare block which is clamped in a vise, as in detail B. The tool is driven in up to its shoulder. After cleaning the surfaces to be soldered to a bright finish, using emery cloth or steel wool, flux is applied and sweat-soldering is done as previously described under "Solder-type fittings." A swedged joint should not be made where a bend is to be located, as the double wall thickness will make bending difficult. Also, a swedged joint should not be made within 4 in. from an end which is to be flared, as the joint will interfere with clamping the tube in the flare block.

Lead pipe: Lead is subject to less corrosion than other metals commonly used for drainage lines. The original lead plumbing of many early American homes is still in use today. Being flexible, lead pipe is particularly suited where building settlement, vibration, or expansion and contraction impose a strain on plumbing fixtures and rigid pipe connections: for example, bathtubs and water closets. Lead waste, vent and drum-trap connections remain watertight under normal conditions. Fig. 32 shows a lead bend installed between a water closet and rigid soil pipe. As lead pipe is easily bent for changes of direction, and can be installed without bulky joint connections and intricate pipe fitting, its use is especially desirable in restricted spaces.

Lead pipe that runs horizontally should be supported, its entire length if possible, by using wooden strips or metal troughs fastened to joists or hung from ceilings with hangers. Vertical runs should be supported at intervals of about 4 ft., using tabs sol-

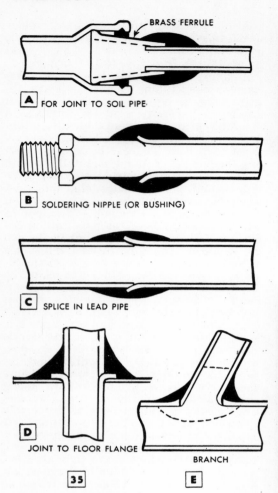

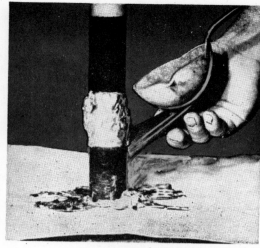

Lead Industries Assn. photos

36

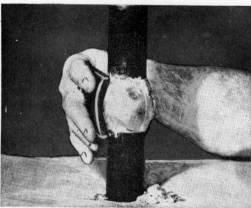

37

A FOR JOINT TO SOIL PIPE

B SOLDERING NIPPLE (OR BUSHING)

C SPLICE IN LEAD PIPE

D JOINT TO FLOOR FLANGE

BRANCH

E

35

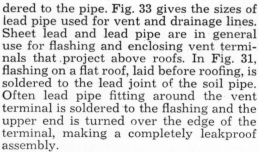

HERRINGBONE TICKING

38

dered to the pipe. Fig. 33 gives the sizes of lead pipe used for vent and drainage lines. Sheet lead and lead pipe are in general use for flashing and enclosing vent terminals that project above roofs. In Fig. 31, flashing on a flat roof, laid before roofing, is soldered to the lead joint of the soil pipe. Often lead pipe fitting around the vent terminal is soldered to the flashing and the upper end is turned over the edge of the terminal, making a completely leakproof assembly.

Another common application of lead pipe in heavier wall thicknesses is for "gooseneck" connections between city water mains and house-service pipes as in Fig. 34. These connections are commonly used in many cities. Alkaline water in contact with lead produces a coating of insoluble lead carbonate, which prevents this water from dissolving lead and becoming toxic. The opposite is the case when lead pipe is used for soft water containing dissolved oxygen, carbon dioxide and organic acids. Therefore lead pipe is not recommended for use as water supply and distribution lines

where the water is to be used for drinking and cooking purposes.

Connecting lead pipes to iron pipes: Fig. 35 shows a number of lead-pipe joints, all of which are made by wiping molten lead around the connection. Detail A shows how a lead pipe is attached to soil pipe by means of a brass calking ferrule. A lead closet sleeve or bend is connected to the hub of

CAST-IRON, HUB AND SPIGOT SOIL PIPE

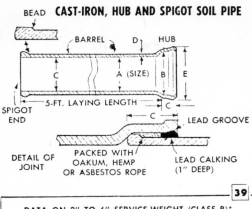

BEAD

BARREL — D HUB

C — A (SIZE) — B E

5-FT. LAYING LENGTH — C

SPIGOT END

DETAIL OF JOINT — PACKED WITH OAKUM, HEMP OR ASBESTOS ROPE — LEAD GROOVE — LEAD CALKING (1" DEEP)

39

DATA ON 2" TO 6" SERVICE-WEIGHT (CLASS B)*						
Nom.	Dimensions (In.)			Lbs. Per Joint		
Size A	B	C	D	E	Oakum	Lead
2	2.94	2.44	.10	3.68	.21	1½ - 2
3	3.94	2.68	.12	4.80	.31	2¼ - 3
4	4.94	2.94	.12	5.80	.42	3 - 4
5	5.95	2.94	.12	6.80	.52	3¾ - 5
6	6.94	2.94	.12	7.80	.63	4½ - 6
* Also Furnished in "Extra-Heavy" Weight						

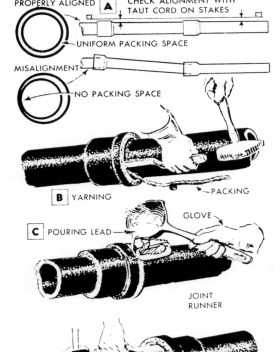

PROPERLY ALIGNED **A** CHECK ALIGNMENT WITH TAUT CORD ON STAKES

UNIFORM PACKING SPACE

MISALIGNMENT

NO PACKING SPACE

B YARNING — PACKING

C POURING LEAD — GLOVE

JOINT RUNNER

D CALKING LEAD

E INSIDE AND OUTSIDE CALKING IRONS

40

soil pipe of the same size by means of an iron Ferrule, which is driven into the pipe, then joint is leaded. Fig. 35B shows lead pipe attached to a brass soldering nipple with which connection is made to a threaded pipe fitting. Soldering bushings are similar except that pipe screws into them. The lead pipe slips into, over or against the ends of these fittings, after which the two are joined with a wiped joint. Joints of lead pipe to brass and copper pipe are made in the same manner. Detail C shows an end-to-end joint in lead pipe. Note how one edge is tapered on the outside so that it fits snugly into a flared and chamfered inside end of the joining length. Tapering is done with a rasp and flaring with a bell-shaped wooden plug of proper size driven into the end of the pipe with a hammer. Detail D shows a joint to a floor flange, and detail E shows a branch connection joined at an angle.

Wiped joints: A wiped joint must have an exposed surface extending not less than ¾ in. on either side of a joint, and the thickest portion should not be less than the thickness of the materials being joined. To make a good wiped joint requires skill and practice. It is done by thoroughly scraping the surfaces to be covered so that they are bright after a coating of plumber's soil (mixture of lampblack and glue) has been applied and allowed to dry. Then saltless mutton tallow is rubbed on the lead surface, and soldering flux on the brass or copper surface, these having been previously cleaned with emery cloth or steel wool. The tallow keeps the lead from oxidizing and also acts as a flux for molten solder, which is poured on slowly from a ladle as in Fig. 36. Although not shown, gloves should be worn. A wiping pad (herringbone ticking folded to several thicknesses) is held under the joint to catch the solder running down and at the same time to shape the joint. Grease on the wiping pad will prevent solder from adhering to it. After the solder joint has been built up, the surface is wiped smooth as in Fig. 37. It is easier to make a wiped point when the pipe is horizontal, in which case it can often be laid on blocks as shown in Fig. 38. A good solder for wiped joints consists of 37 percent tin and 63 percent lead. When melted for application, it should be just hot enough to scorch a piece of paper.

Cast-iron hub-and-spigot soil pipe: Coated with coal-tar pitch to make it acid-resisting, cast-iron soil pipe of the hub-and-spigot type, Fig. 39, is most commonly used for underground drainage lines within a building; also this type can be used for the soil stack and the drainage lines from water closets to the stack. Often this pipe is used also for house sewers. It is furnished in 5-ft. lengths (laying lengths), in sizes from 2 to 15 in. nominal inside diameter. The 3 to 6-in. sizes are most common. Lengths having a hub at each end are furnished also. These are convenient and economical since two short lengths of pipe can often be cut from one double-hub length instead of cutting these from two regular lengths.

Assembling soil pipe: When assembled, the spigot end of the soil pipe faces the direction of flow and fits into the hub end (also called "bell" end) of the next length. Before joining pipes, each length should be tested by striking it lightly with a hammer at the ends. A clear bell-like ring indicates that the pipe is not cracked. The spigot end has a bead which fits snugly into a hub so that packing material will not be forced inside the pipe. Joining ends should be thoroughly clean and dry, and the two joining lengths should be in perfect alignment, which can be checked with a taut cord tied to two stakes as in Fig. 40A. Misalignment in length causes misalignment at joints so that the space between pipe and hub (annular space) is not uniform in width.

The proper method of making a good joint starts with a packing of oakum, hemp or asbestos rope, which is wrapped around the pipe and is driven down with a yarning iron and hammer as in detail B. Work around the pipe evenly so that the packing is not forced tightly on one side while it is still loose on the other. This causes the pipe to shift off center. The packing should come to an inch from the rim of the hub to leave enough space for leading, which anchors in the hub groove. Strands of the packing should not project out of the hub as this may cause leakage. For pipe laid horizontally you need an asbestos joint runner to hold molten lead in the joint, detail C. Its use is explained in the tool section. A joint runner is not needed when pouring lead into a joint on vertical pipe.

Calking lead is used for this purpose, obtainable in 3 to 5-lb. cakes and in 90 to 100-lb. pigs. Amounts of lead and oakum required for filling soil-pipe joints are given in Fig. 39. The lead is melted in a fire pot. Correct temperature for pouring is indicated when the molt becomes cherry red. Then a ladle is used to pour the joint as in Fig. 40C. Before melting lead and using a ladle read instructions and precautions contained in the tool section. The entire joint should be filled at one pouring. When the lead hardens, the joint runner is removed. As lead shrinks slightly upon cooling, it must be tamped into firm contact with the pipe and hub, detail D. For this you use a light hammer and calking irons as shown in detail E. Avoid heavy blows which may

CUTTING SOIL PIPE

41

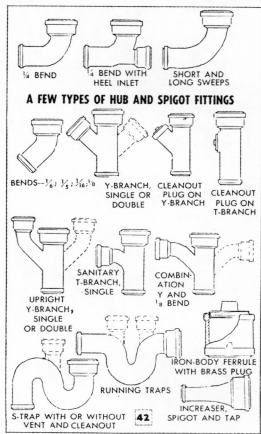

¼ BEND   ¼ BEND WITH HEEL INLET   SHORT AND LONG SWEEPS

A FEW TYPES OF HUB AND SPIGOT FITTINGS

BENDS—⅙; ⅕; ¹⁄₁₆; ⅛   Y-BRANCH, SINGLE OR DOUBLE   CLEANOUT PLUG ON Y-BRANCH   CLEANOUT PLUG ON T-BRANCH

SANITARY T-BRANCH, SINGLE   COMBINATION Y AND ⅛ BEND

UPRIGHT Y-BRANCH, SINGLE OR DOUBLE

IRON-BODY FERRULE WITH BRASS PLUG

RUNNING TRAPS

S-TRAP WITH OR WITHOUT VENT AND CLEANOUT   42   INCREASER, SPIGOT AND TAP

loosen rather than tighten the lead ring. Go around the joint with an "inside" calking iron to pack the lead against the pipe and an "outside" iron to pack it against the hub. When molten lead cannot be used, as for example under water or where the use of an open flame is dangerous, lead wool, which comes in ropelike form, is used. This is simply packed into a homogeneous ring, without the need of heat. Some codes, however, do not permit its use as a substitute for melted-lead joints in ordinary soil-pipe installations.

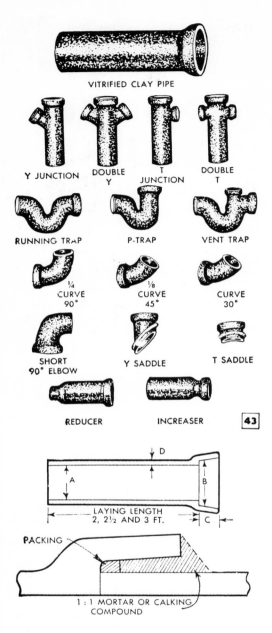

VITRIFIED CLAY PIPE

Y JUNCTION   DOUBLE Y   T JUNCTION   DOUBLE T

RUNNING TRAP   P-TRAP   VENT TRAP

¼ CURVE 90°   ⅛ CURVE 45°   CURVE 30°

SHORT 90° ELBOW   Y SADDLE   T SADDLE

REDUCER   INCREASER   **43**

LAYING LENGTH 2, 2½ AND 3 FT.

PACKING

1:1 MORTAR OR CALKING COMPOUND

Size A	B	C	D	E	F	G	H
DATA ON STANDARD-STRENGTH VITRIFIED-CLAY PIPE							
4	5¾	1¾	½	9	1430	.074	.44
6	8	2¼	⅝	15	1430	.234	.86
8	10½	2½	¾	24	1430	.365	1.13

E   AVERAGE WEIGHT PER FT. OF LENGTH.
F   CRUSHING STRENGTH PER LINEAL FT. ON SAND-BEARING PIPE.
G   POUNDS OF JUTE (AT 25 LBS. PER CU. FT.) REQUIRED PER JOINT.
H   POUNDS OF ASPHALT JOINT COMPOUND (AT 90 LBS. PER CU. FT.) REQUIRED PER JOINT.

44

Cutting soil pipe: A cold chisel and a hammer are used to cut soil pipe as shown in Fig. 41. First the pipe is marked with chalk so that the cut end will be square. Then the pipe is scored all around by tapping the chisel lightly. In doing so the chisel should be pointed toward the center of the pipe and moved forward in overlapping steps for successive blows. After scoring the pipe, it is placed on a support such as a wooden block or sandbag set directly under the point of cutting, and it is struck with increasingly heavier blows along the score. An even break usually occurs after circling the pipe a few times. Actually the pipe is not cut through but the narrow strip of metal along the score is weakened until it breaks. The same method is used also for vitrified-clay pipe.

Cast-iron soil-pipe fittings: Fig. 42 shows a variety of fittings for cast-iron soil pipe. These have ends to match the pipe and are joined in similar manner. For changes of direction, bends and sweeps are used. Their angle is not designated in degrees but by fractions of 360 deg. Thus a 90 deg. turn is called a ¼ bend; a 60 deg. turn a ⅙ bend; a 45 deg. turn is a ⅛ bend. Long-sweep turns offer least resistance to the drainage flow.

Vitrified-clay pipe: The smooth surface of vitrified-clay pipe does not wear or corrode, being inert to acids, alkalies and solvents. Other advantages of this pipe are its low cost, simplicity of installation, and its permanence when not subjected to abnormal strains that may crack or break it. It is furnished in 2, 2½ and 3-ft. laying lengths; in 4 to 36-in. nominal inside diameters; in two grades (standard and extra-strength); and in straight and curved lengths of various shapes, some of which are shown in Fig. 43. One end of each length is a hub or socket and fits over the spigot or plain end of an adjacent length as in Fig. 44, which also gives data on this kind of pipe as well as the amount of jute and calking compound required per joint.

Vitrified-clay pipe can be cut in the same way as cast-iron soil pipe. It can be connected to the latter of same size by using an increaser. Joints can be sealed with portland-cement mortar, or with asphalt-base jointing compounds. The ends should be thoroughly cleaned and free from grease or oil. After carefully aligning two adjoining lengths, the spigot end being inserted as far as possible in the hub, you lightly tamp in enough oakum or jute, about ½ in. thick, to seal the joint so that cement or melted compound will not seep through to the inside. The packing is done evenly from all sides to keep the joining sections in concentric alignment. Often packing is omitted, and only a rather stiff mortar is used, in which case the pipe is swabbed out.

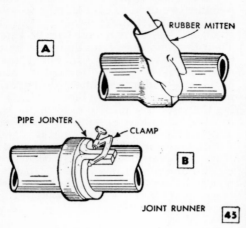

Mortar joints: After packing a joint with oakum, force into the joint a 1:1 mix of clean, sharp sand and portland cement, with just enough water added to make a rather stiff paste that will not run. A wooden calking tool will help to push the cement down solidly into the joint. The surplus is rounded off neatly with a trowel or a rubber mitten as in detail A of Fig. 45. Often two or three lengths of pipe are set up vertically, Fig. 46, for making joints with mortar that is plastic enough to be poured. This leaves fewer joints to be made in the trench. After letting the cement harden overnight, the pipe is carried by a stout pole slipped through it, after which it is lowered into the trench and joined to other similar lengths.

Other jointing compounds: A number of asphalt-base and other compounds are available for making good joints that remain slightly flexible and resist root penetration. Most of these compounds are poured while hot into thoroughly clean and dry joints after tamping in a seal of jute, oakum or asbestos rope. The melted compound can be poured into joints when several lengths are stacked vertically as in Fig. 46, but when joints on horizontal lengths are poured, a "joint runner," detail B, Fig. 45, or a clay dam is used. Compounds should be used in accordance with manufacturer's instructions. If they are overheated or kept hot too long they may become brittle. If not sufficiently heated, they may harden before the joint is completed. During cold weather they may not adhere effectively unless the pipe jointing is preheated.

Concrete pipe: Also shaped with hub and spigot ends, concrete pipe that is used for drainage purposes comes in 2, 2½, 3 and 4-ft. lengths, and in 4 to 24-in. nominal inside diameters. It is assembled in the same way as vitrified-clay pipe. Concrete pipe is subject to attack by acids and is

not as durable as vitrified-clay pipe for use as sewers, although its cost is approximately the same.

Asbestos-cement pipe: This pipe is hard, dense and strong, as the mixture from which it is made—asbestos fiber, portland cement and silica—is subjected to heavy pressure during manufacture. Being durable and highly resistant to corrosion, this pipe has been found successful as vent and sewer pipe. It is furnished in 5 and 10-ft. lengths, the advantage of the latter being that fewer joints are required. Although sizes range from 6 to 36 in. in diameter, the smaller sizes, from 2 to 6 in., are used for house sewers, Fig. 47, and vent pipes, Fig. 48.

Ends of the pipe are machined to take couplings of the same material. The use of special rubber rings between couplings and pipes, as shown in Figs. 49 and 50, gives a tight, flexible joint especially designed to overcome leakage and root penetration. Pipe and couplings are easily assembled by pressing them together as shown in Fig. 51, using the simple arrangement shown in Fig. 52.

A number of T and Y branches are furnished, as well as elbows, bends and special adapters to make connections to other pipes such as soil pipe. Where short lengths are required to make closures, the pipe can be sawed off with a carpenter's saw. Adapters are also furnished to join such a cut end to a machined end, or to join two cut ends together. In this case a seal is

Johns-Manville photos

47

48

49

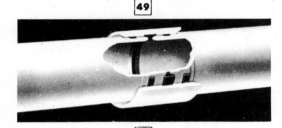

50

51

made with cement, lead or other commercial jointing compound. Fig. 53 gives some data on dimensions and weight of house sewer and vent pipes made of asbestos cement.

Porous and perforated pipe: For disposal lines of septic tanks and for rapid drainage of ground water, porous drain tile is most extensively used. It comes in 1-ft. lengths and the 4 to 6-in. sizes are most common. The pipe is of uniform diameter and has no hub. The lengths are laid end-to-end, with tar-paper squares over the joints to prevent entrance of soil. Perforated pipe of vitrified clay and bituminized fiber is also made for this purpose.

53 ASBESTOS-CEMENT PIPE

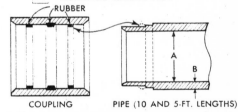

RUBBER

A

B

COUPLING PIPE (10 AND 5-FT. LENGTHS)

Nom. Size A		Thickness B	Weight C	Strength D
Sewer Pipe 1	Vent Pipe 2			
4		.27	4.7	1740
5		.30	6.3	1680
6		.30	7.5	1420
	2	.30	2.2	
	3	.32	3.2	
	4	.32	4.2	

1—PIPE FOR HOUSE-TO-SEWER CONNECTIONS; SIMILAR PIPE ALSO FURNISHED UP TO 36" DIA., IN TWO CLASSES AND IN 13-FT. LENGTHS
2—PIPE FOR VENTS IN HOUSE PLUMBING; HAS DIFFERENT STYLE JOINT THAN ONE ILLUSTRATED. OTHER PIPE FURNISHED FOR FLUES
C—WEIGHT IN LBS. PER FT. PER 10-FT. LENGTH WITH COUPLINGS
D—MINIMUM APPLIED LOADS (LBS. PER FT.) FOR CRUSHING TESTS

LEVER

PIPE CLIP

WOOD SCREWS PUSHER PLATE

52

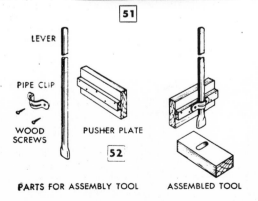

PARTS FOR ASSEMBLY TOOL ASSEMBLED TOOL

54

55

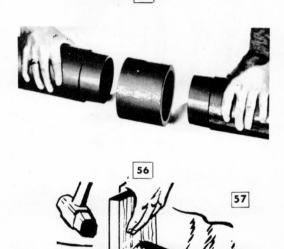

56

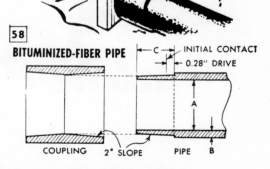

57

Bituminized-fiber pipe: Fiber pipe has been successfully used for many years for numerous purposes such as house sewers, outside downspouts, conductor pipe for irrigation and for farm and ranch gravity-type water supply and distribution lines. It is impregnated throughout with coal-tar pitch, is lightweight, non-corrosive and slightly flexible, which allows it to absorb shocks, earth tremors and normal soil movement without cracking, shearing off or pulling out at the joints. Sweeps of 45 and 90 deg., as well as numerous other fittings are furnished. Fig. 54 shows this pipe used in a house-sewer installation.

The pipes have tapered ends which are joined to couplings having slight inside tapers to match, Fig. 56. Driven together simply by using a block and hammer as in Fig. 57, the joints are so tight that tree roots cannot enter. Connections can be made to other pipes, either the threaded or the hub-and-spigot type, by means of special adapters. Joints to cast-iron soil pipe are sealed with flexible jointing compounds, molten lead or lead wool, as previously described under cast-iron and vitrified-clay pipe. Fig. 55 shows how an ordinary handsaw is used to cut fiber pipe to any length. A special cutter is required to taper ends cut in this manner, but where such a cutter is not available, these ends can be tightly sealed in a special coupling with the aid of jointing compound. Fig. 58 gives dimensional data on the smaller sizes of bituminized-fiber pipe.

Methods of supporting pipe: Pipes and tubing used in a plumbing system must be installed with adequate support to prevent undue strains and stresses on it. In a building, pipe is "hung" in pipe supports so that contraction, expansion and settling of the building will not break the pipe or place a strain on it. Pipe should not be attached rigidly to a building. Fig. 59 shows several

58

BITUMINIZED-FIBER PIPE

COUPLING   2° SLOPE   PIPE

INITIAL CONTACT — 0.28" DRIVE

SIZE A (In.)	THICKN. B (Min.) (In.)	C (In.)	Length (Feet)	Weight D	Strength E
2	.23	1.43	5	1.24	1100
3	.28	1.69	8	1.71	1100
4	.32	1.94	8	2.66	1100
5	.41	1.94	5	4.44	1300
6	.46	1.94	5	5.78	1300
8	.57	2.48	5	9.81	1600

D—Weight Per Ft. Including Couplings
E—Crushing Strength Between Two Flat Plates

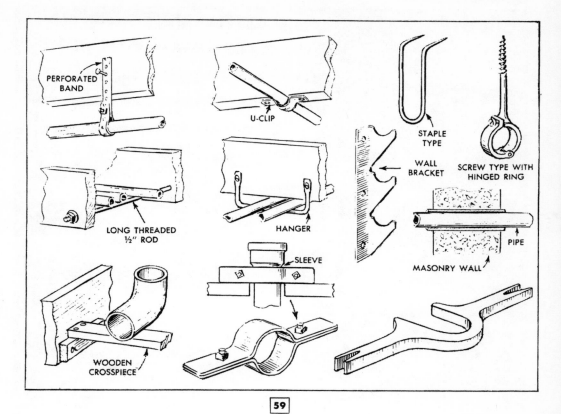

59

methods of supporting pipes. The use of pipe straps is the most common. Spacing of the supports must be such that the pipe will not sag. Screwed pipe should be supported at intervals not over 12 ft. Copper tubing should be supported at intervals not over 6 ft. for piping 1½ in. and smaller, and not over 10 ft. for sizes 2 in. and larger. Supports for cast-iron soil pipe should not be spaced more than 5 ft. apart, and should be placed as near to the joint of the pipe as possible. Lead pipe is laid on strips of wood or metal, or is otherwise suitably supported its entire length.

Vertical lengths of pipe may be supported by collars, yokes or tabs. Distances between such supports should not be more than one-and-one-half-story height for screwed pipe, one-story height for cast-iron soil pipe, one-story height for copper tubing 1½ in. and over in size. For copper tubing smaller than 1¼ in., and also for lead pipe, the spacing between supports should not exceed 4 ft.

Pipe hangers should be attached securely to the building construction, using nails, screws or bolts in wood, and screws or bolts driven into metal expansion sleeves for proper anchorage in masonry. Attachment of hangers to wooden plugs driven into holes drilled in masonry is not dependable as the plugs may shrink and loosen. Buried pipe should be laid on compact earth. In filled and other unstable earth, pipe other than cast-iron soil pipe should be supported on concrete pads suitably spaced to prevent settling.

Dimension Table for Standard Pipe Minimizes Measuring Errors

When making plumbing or heating repairs in the home, costly waste of pipe is likely to result from inaccurate measurements, such as, forgetting to allow for the threaded ends of the pipe inside the fittings. This table, which gives pipe diameters and thread lengths in fractions of an inch, will help you obtain correct measurements.

PIPE SIZE	⅛"	¼"	⅜"	½"	¾"	1"	1¼"	1½"	2"
INSIDE DIAMETER	9/32"	3/8"	1/2"	5/8"	13/16"	1 1/32"	1 3/8"	1 5/8"	2 1/16"
OUTSIDE DIAMETER	13/32"	17/32"	11/16"	27/32"	1 1/16"	1 5/16"	1 21/32"	1 29/32"	2 3/8"
APPROXIMATE THREAD LENGTH ONE END	¼"	3/8"	3/8"	½"	9/16"	11/16"	11/16"	11/16"	¾"
APPROXIMATE THREAD LENGTH BOTH ENDS	½"	¾"	¾"	1"	1⅛"	1⅜"	1⅜"	1⅜"	1½"

PLUMBING REPAIRS MADE SIMPLE
Water-System Troubles and Cures

MOST WATER-SYSTEM TROUBLES can be prevented by proper servicing, such as keeping faucets and valves in good condition, renewing air in air chambers, protecting pipes against frost, and avoiding scale accumulations by water-softening equipment. Inherent troubles that are due to faulty installation may necessitate replacement of pipe and fittings. Substitution of larger pipe may also be necessary to take care of added demands.

Faucet noises: Chattering and whistling at faucets are among the most common noises. When this occurs with a compression-type faucet as shown in Fig. 1, look for a loose or defective internal assembly. Often the trouble is caused by a loose washer, which can produce chattering by alternately closing and freeing the water flow when turned on slightly. To remove the faucet spindle assembly, first turn off the water supply, then wrap the cap nut with **cardboard** or cloth to protect its finish when

loosening it with a suitable wrench—not a pipe wrench or pliers. Back off the cap nut entirely and unscrew the spindle assembly in the same direction as the handle turns when opening the faucet. Check the small screw holding the washer on the end of the spindle. If loose, tighten it so that the washer is seated firmly. If the washer is worn, replace it with a new one. When screwing the spindle assembly back into the faucet, carefully check whether there is any up-and-down play caused by wear on the threaded parts. If so, replace the spindle with a faucet insert.

Chattering and whistling noises may occur also in faucets and valves of poor hydraulic design, especially cheaper ones, due to a small, restricted waterway. When a water passage is restricted, the velocity of flow through the restricted passage is increased. When fast-moving water changes in direction, centrifugal force creates a vacuum at the inside of the turn and may

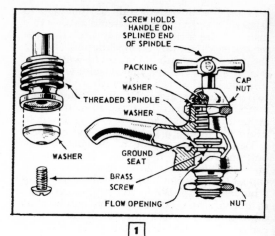

1

2

cause vapor bubbles to form. When these collapse the vibration results in noise; if the vibration is of high frequency, whistling results; if of low frequency, chattering and pounding result. Where such noise in faucets and valves is inherent due to poor design, about the only remedy is to replace them.

When noise occurs in a Fuller-type faucet (see *Faucets*), which is now practically obsolete but still is found in old plumbing systems, the body of the faucet is unscrewed from the tailpiece. The ball inside may be loose and require tightening, or the ball shaft and spindle eccentric may be worn, permitting the assembly to rattle.

Water hammer in pipes: Hammering noises in pipes that occur when a faucet or valve is closed suddenly are also extremely common. The momentum of fast-moving water in a pipe, particularly in a long horizontal pipe where water has considerable velocity, causes a shock wave when suddenly arrested. The shock wave travels back and forth between the faucet or valve and the point where the pipe changes direction or connects to a larger pipe or to a tank. The hammering that this causes can also shake the pipe violently. Such strain can result in rupture of the pipe at fittings, or the fittings themselves can crack. This is one reason why only malleable-iron fittings should be used on water pipes. Sometimes the noise is less pronounced when the pipe is anchored securely, but the same pressure is created by the shock wave and may still be injurious to the plumbing system although perhaps to a lesser extent. Water hammer is most pronounced when it occurs in hard, rigid pipe such as iron, steel or brass. It is less noticeable in flexible pipes such as copper, lead and especially plastic pipe, as it is very flexible and offers relief from pressure.

Since the trouble is occasioned by sudden closing of faucets and valves during the last 15 percent of the closing swing, it can be eliminated by closing them slowly. It cannot be prevented in quick-acting automatic valves generally, or in self-closing faucets. Any or all of the three following methods are used to reduce or eliminate water hammer: (1) Proper servicing of existing air chambers, or the installation of larger ones; (2) by using a pressure-reducing valve or regulator; (3) by providing braces to prevent pipe movement.

Servicing air chambers: In every well-designed plumbing system, air chambers are installed near outlets as in Figs. 2 and 3. The purpose is to provide a pressure relief. When faucets or valves are closed quickly, water rushes into the air chamber. As air is compressible it cushions the water thrust to a more gentle stop and thus causes less shock. However, since the air cushion is gradually absorbed by the water under pressure, more air must be provided periodically. This is done by draining out the water that replaces the air in a waterlogged air chamber as follows: First shut off the water supply to the air chamber at the nearest branch control valve, then open a drain valve below the level of the air chamber. If the air chamber is located above the faucet level as in the case with those

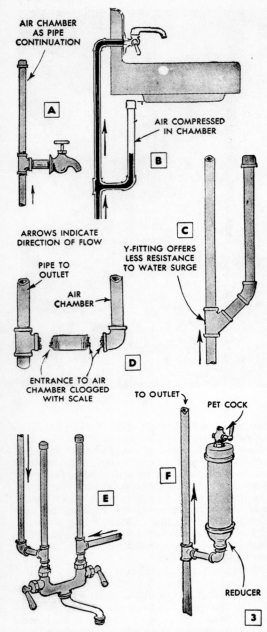

AIR CHAMBER
AS PIPE
CONTINUATION

A

AIR COMPRESSED
IN CHAMBER

B

ARROWS INDICATE
DIRECTION OF FLOW

C

Y-FITTING OFFERS
LESS RESISTANCE
TO WATER SURGE

PIPE TO
OUTLET

AIR
CHAMBER

D

ENTRANCE TO AIR
CHAMBER CLOGGED
WITH SCALE

TO OUTLET

PET COCK

F

E

REDUCER

3

on basement laundry tubs, Fig. 2 and Fig. 3E, the faucet will serve as a drain. If the air chamber is accessible, remove the cap on the upper end to assure that water will run out—especially from small pipes which sometimes retain water unless it is so released. If there is any evidence of scale and corrosion in pipes, the air chambers should be removed occasionally to check whether they become open. Sometimes they become clogged, especially in short horizontal parts, detail D. When reassembling, wipe some pipe-joint compound or white

lead on the threaded ends of the pipe to assure air-tight joints, but avoid getting this inside of the fittings or it may taint the water. It may also start an obstruction. Repeat the process for both hot and cold-water outlets. If a pipe cap fits too loosely, wrap the threaded end of the pipe with a strand or two of cotton string or No. 40 cotton thread.

An air chamber that requires frequent attention can be made more convenient to drain by adding a petcock on the cap and a T-fitting with a plug or petcock at the bottom. Another method of servicing an air chamber is to install a tire valve on the cap so that air can be replenished by using a bicycle pump. When the supply of water to an individual faucet or valve can be shut off at a point close to the air chamber, you can remove the air chamber to drain it.

Air-chamber design: The capacity of an air chamber should not be less than 1 percent of the capacity of the pipe line in which water hammer occurs. For the average home, air chambers should not be less than 18 in. long. They should be made of 1-in. pipe when installed on ½-in. water lines, and of 1¼-in. pipe when installed on ¾-in. lines—two pipe sizes larger than the line. See Fig. 3F. Air chambers are set vertically; they may be a continuation of a riser as in detail A, or can be offset as in details B, C, E and F. Where possible, an air chamber arranged as a continuation of the pipe is best as it receives the full thrust of the water. For offset arrangements, 45-deg. fittings, as in detail C, offer less resistance to thrust than 90-deg. fittings. The direction of flow may be downward, as in detail E, but in all cases the opening to the air chamber is at its bottom. It has been found that the effectiveness of air chambers is measurably increased if the inlet opening is restricted to about one-half the internal diameter of the water pipe to which the air chamber is connected.

Pressure-relieving devices: There are also a number of commercially made shock absorbers which serve the same purpose as air chambers. Some of these have metal bellows; others, like the one in Fig. 4, have spring-loaded diaphragms. This type requires only a few inches of vertical space and is very convenient for use where overhead clearance is limited. Among the advantages of these shock absorbers are that they require much less space than air chambers and do not require periodic draining like the latter.

Location of air chambers and shock absorbers: Air chambers may be installed in partitions near the outlets they serve. They can also be located under the outlets, as in cabinets under kitchen sinks, or they may be located in an accessible position above outlets, as with faucets on basement laundry tubs. Where water hammer occurs in the service line from street to house, a large air chamber, having provisions for venting and draining, should be located at the service-line entrance as shown in Fig. 5. When long, horizontal pipes require air chambers or shock absorbers these are installed at the end toward which water flows.

Pressure-reducing valves: Where water pressure is high, a pressure-reducing valve or pressure regulator, described under *Valves and Faucets,* can be used to reduce or eliminate water hammer. By reducing the pressure, the velocity of water flow is slowed down and less shock is produced when faucets and valves are closed suddenly. If the trouble is not entirely cured by means of such a regulator, air chambers or pressure-relief devices may be installed also.

Pipe supports: Excessive lengthwise movement of long horizontal pipes can be avoided by supporting them firmly as shown in details A, B and C of Fig. 6. Such support does not in any way reduce the shock wave caused by closing faucets and valves suddenly, and therefore does not prevent possible injury to them. As the pipe is braced at the end toward which water flows, movement in the opposite direction due to expansion and contraction is not restricted.

Rattling of loose pipe against walls or joists can be prevented by proper support. Strap-type pipe hangers should be attached securely to the pipe; they can swing slightly to allow for pipe expansion. Pipe clips of the kind shown in detail D are used for supporting risers. They should not be used for attaching pipe to joists; then vibration is conducted to floors and noise is intensified. On concrete walls, pipe is attached at suitable points to blocks as shown.

Noises from water heaters: Rumbling and pounding noises sometimes originate from water heaters or from the pipes between heaters and tanks. If a water heater is not properly protected by means of a safety-relief valve, or if the valve is not functioning, such noises may be caused by overheated water. The heater should be turned off at once and the relief valve checked. Some relief valves have test levers operated manually to make this check.

Noises in a water-heating system that is properly protected may also be due to poor circulation between the heater or furnace water back and the storage tank. Heavy liming of a heater coil or furnace water back, or the pipe from heater to storage tank, particularly at fittings, may restrict the circulation so much that steam pockets are formed. When these come in contact with the colder water of the tank, they collapse and cause hammering. The

Josam Mfg. Co. photo

4

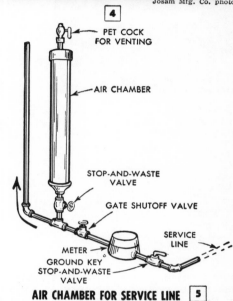

PET COCK FOR VENTING

AIR CHAMBER

STOP-AND-WASTE VALVE

GATE SHUTOFF VALVE

SERVICE LINE

METER

GROUND KEY STOP-AND-WASTE VALVE

AIR CHAMBER FOR SERVICE LINE **5**

same can occur when a furnace coil is not level. This may loosen or break pipe joints and cause leakage.

Water-heater noises also can be traced to faulty pipe arrangements or pipe of insufficient size as, for instance, when an upper connection the shape of an inverted U retards circulation. To a lesser extent, the same condition occurs in an L connection—the lower line may become clogged and will then impede circulation. All of these connections allow hot water to be forced into the tank in spurts when pressure is built up behind it. Usually water-heater noises are easy to avoid if unimpeded circulation of water is assured by proper connections, adequate pipe size and clean, internal surfaces in the heating coils and pipes. Also, the provision of an air chamber or shock absorber in the line from a water-heating coil to a storage tank will generally reduce the noise.

Water-closet noises: Many water closets emit a high-pitched noise that sometimes becomes a whistle when a flush tank is being filled. This originates at restricted passages in a float valve, particularly with

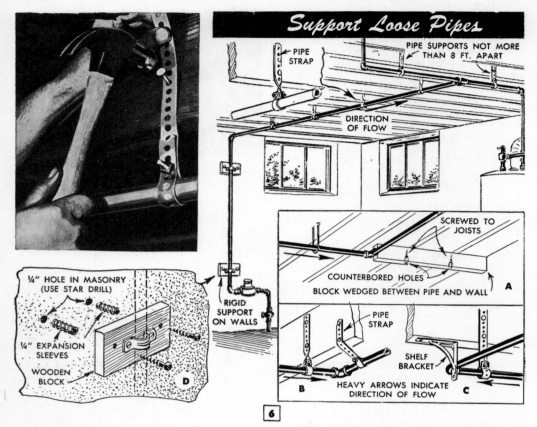

Support Loose Pipes

PIPE STRAP

PIPE SUPPORTS NOT MORE THAN 8 FT. APART

DIRECTION OF FLOW

SCREWED TO JOISTS

COUNTERBORED HOLES

BLOCK WEDGED BETWEEN PIPE AND WALL

A

PIPE STRAP

SHELF BRACKET

RIGID SUPPORT ON WALLS

¼" HOLE IN MASONRY (USE STAR DRILL)

¼" EXPANSION SLEEVES

WOODEN BLOCK

D

B

HEAVY ARROWS INDICATE DIRECTION OF FLOW

C

6

cheaper-type valves. Sometimes the condition can be remedied by proper adjustment of the valve. If not, the valve should be replaced with one that is more silent. If a float valve is provided with a backflow preventer or vacuum breaker, this sometimes causes a clicking sound. A low humming noise often indicates that water is running into the bowl after the tank has been filled, likely due to a leaky discharge valve. Usually the cause is a worn stopper ball but sometimes the seat is covered with grit or is pitted from corrosion. A new ball is the prescribed remedy, but the seat may also need cleaning and smoothing with emery cloth. More information on water-closet valves is given in *Valves and Faucets*.

High-velocity noises in pipes: Whistling noises often are caused by high velocity of water flowing through pipes. The noise is produced when water flows around bends at high speed, the pressure at the inside of the turn being reduced by centrifugal force. The smaller the pipe is, the faster the water flows when submitted to the same pressure as in a larger pipe. Thus smaller pipes cause more noise than larger ones. Often the noise can be reduced or eliminated by simply wrapping the pipe, if accessible, with several layers of hair felt,

other sound-proofing material or by replacing the pipe with one of larger size. Floors and walls often act as sounding boards that intensify such noises. For this reason direct contact with a plastered wall, floor or joists under floors should be avoided.

Leaky faucets and water closets: Fig. 7 gives the cost of water leaks, which shows that it pays to prevent them. Leaks at faucets may be caused by a loose cap nut, worn packing in the nut, by a worn washer or washer seat. Methods of repair are given in *Faucets*. Water closets may develop leaks where the bowl connects to the soil pipe, usually indicated by water on the floor around this connection. The remedy consists of removing the bowl and resealing the joint as described in *Drainage*. Leaks may also occur between the tank and the bowl. They may be at the gasket between the tank and bowl if these are close-coupled or at the slip-joint elbow or sleeve between tank and bowl. Usually a new washer or gasket will cure the trouble. Another point where leakage may develop is at the joint between the float-valve stem and the tank, or at the point where it connects to the water-supply pipe. Assembly of the valve stem with the tank and pipe is shown in Fig. 15 of *Faucets*.

SIZE OF LEAK	CU. FT. PER DAY	COST PER YEAR AT		RATE PER 100 CU. FT.
..... STEADY DROP	3	$2.16		
• ¼₄	6	$4.32	1st 10 M CU. FT.	18c
• ¹⁄₃₂	23	$15.12	2nd 40 M CU. FT.	12c
● ¹⁄₁₆	93		OVER 50 M CU. FT.	9c
● ¹⁄₁₆	93	$60.48		
⬤ ⅛	400			$196.80

7

Pipe leaks: When leaks develop at the threaded joints of pipe, the joint is either loose or the pipe may be fractured. Slightly loose joints often become sealed by scale and rust formation. If the leak persists and is located within a reasonable distance from a union, or from the end of a pipe, it can be unscrewed and examined. Sometimes reassembling it after the threads have been coated with pipe-joint compound will make it leakproof. However, the threads on a pipe or those of a fitting may be defective or the fitting may be cracked and require replacement. Fractures from strain on pipes usually occur at the ends where the wall thickness has been reduced and weakened by threading, especially where threads have not been cut true. Strain on pipes may be caused by constant vibration or water hammer. Another cause of pipe leaks is freezing. Soft copper tubing can be subjected to repeated strains of freezing, enlarging each time, until it hardens and breaks. Flexible plastic pipe is not ruptured by freezing.

To repair a leaky pipe temporarily, you first shut off the water supply, then cut the pipe with a hacksaw on either side of the leak, after which a length of rubber hose or flexible plastic tubing is slipped over the ends as shown in Fig. 8, using hose clamps to tighten it securely. The inside diameter of the hose or tubing must be equal to the outside diameter of the pipe; 1-in. auto hose fits ¾-in. pipe and ¾-in. garden hose fits ½-in. pipe.

Other emergency repairs for leaky pipes are shown in details A, B and C of Fig. 9. Electrician's friction tape may be wrapped tightly around the pipe to 2 in. beyond the leak. The pressure may force water to leak between the pipe and the wrapping, but a slight drip is better than a spray.

The best repair is a permanent one made with pipe as in Figs. 10 and 11. Cut the pipe with a hacksaw to permit unscrewing it, unless a union is located nearby. Saw the pipe not less than 4 in. from a fitting as in detail A of Fig. 11. Then unscrew the cut ends. The new section is made up of two lengths of pipe and a union, which, when assembled, should equal the length of the old pipe. A single length can be installed only when the old length was disconnected at a union as shown in detail B. Sim-

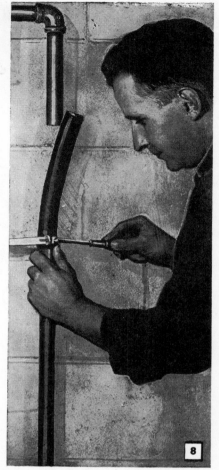

8

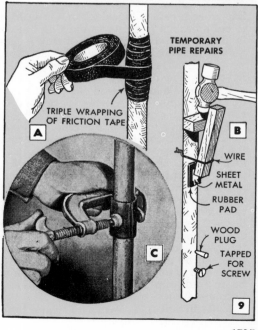

TRIPLE WRAPPING OF FRICTION TAPE

A

C

TEMPORARY PIPE REPAIRS

B

WIRE

SHEET METAL

RUBBER PAD

WOOD PLUG

TAPPED FOR SCREW

9

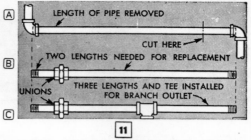

10

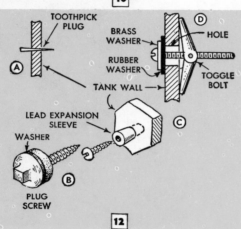

12

ilar procedure is followed when it is desired to cut a branch line into an existing line as in detail C, except that a T-fitting is required between two new pipe lengths, which when assembled should equal the length of the cut pipe.

When a pipe leaks inside of a partition or under a floor, it is generally necessary to remove plaster or a portion of the floor (or ceiling below) to get at the pipe. In some cases a repair can be made by uncovering the leaky pipe at two accessible points near fittings. The pipe then is cut near the fittings, the stub ends are moved and adaptors are used for connecting copper tubing of proper size. Being flexible, copper tubing can often be installed inside partitions and floors through two small openings with the aid of a chain. The old, leaky pipe is left in the partition or under the floor. Plastic pipe can be used instead of copper pipe if it is completely protected from rodents. Some kinds of plastic pipe in exposed locations are subject to rodent attack.

Leaks in tanks: Leaks in a hot-water tank

generally indicate that the inside is badly corroded and weakened, in which case the tank should be replaced. However, an old tank sometimes can be kept in service until a new one is installed by making any of the temporary repairs shown in Fig. 12. If the tank is insulated, the outer covering and the insulation are removed to find and repair the leak. A pin-size leak often can be plugged by driving in the end of a round toothpick as in detail A. Swelling of the wood from its absorption of moisture will keep it in place. Larger leaks may be stopped by driving in a plug screw as in detail B. Another repair consists of drilling or reaming a hole to ¼-in. size to admit a tapered lead expansion plug as in detail C. Driving a screw through the plug expands it. Still another repair method, detail D, is to enlarge the leak enough to permit inserting a toggle bolt to hold a brass-and-rubber washer assembly snugly against the leak on the outside of the tank.

Dripping from condensation: In many localities trouble is experienced from "sweating" pipes—condensation of moisture on the outside. The beads of moisture collect and drop off and may damage tools or other articles underneath such pipes. Normally, water inside a pipe or container warms up to room temperature, at which point condensation on the outside stops. In a plumbing system, cold-water pipes remain cold because water is continually drawn from them so that condensation continues. When this occurs between walls and floors, considerable damage may result to wallpaper and plaster as well as to structural members such as sills and studs, which may deteriorate from rot.

In basements, condensation troubles usually are experienced during the summer months. In closed basements, humidity can be minimized by means of a calcium-chloride drier, Fig. 13, or an electrically operated dehumidifier, Fig. 14. Besides preventing pipes from sweating such control also prevents condensation on cool floors and walls.

Condensation on cold-water pipes can be prevented by covering them with antidrip insulation, which is available in various forms. The pipes can be wrapped with a

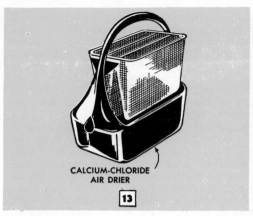

CALCIUM-CHLORIDE
AIR DRIER

13

General Motors Corp., Frigidaire Div. photo

14

thick tape containing ground cork as in Fig. 15, or coated with a thick plastic paint that contains cork granules, Fig. 16. Other coverings are tubular and split lengthwise for quick, easy attachment as shown in Fig. 19. These coverings may be air-cell asbestos, mineral or other wool. They are provided with a waterproof inner liner. Such insulation can be applied to exposed pipe, but hardly to pipe inside of partitions and floors without involving considerable cost and trouble unless installed when a house is being built.

Where much condensation forms on a water-closet tank and it drips on the floor, a tray like that in Fig. 17 can be attached under the tank. Trays on wall-hung tanks have a drain tube leading to the bowl; those on close-coupled tanks are provided with absorbent pads. Some tanks are made with an inner liner, such as shown in Fig. 18, which prevents them from being cooled by the water inside and thus prevents sweating. A water-tempering tank, which should never be insulated, can be provided with a drip pan if moisture on the basement floor is objectionable.

Protecting water pipes from frost: Where water pipes are exposed to low temperatures, they should be protected with insulation of suitable thickness; 1¼-in. felt covering generally is used. The covering must be continuous without any air gaps between adjoining lengths and must be carried over all pipe fittings. The pipe is first wrapped with tar paper, then covered with insulation which is wrapped with canvas as shown in Fig. 20A. Various types of tubular insulation can also be used; in which case the joints also are covered.

Installed pipe that will be exposed to weather must be properly protected. Where pipe is already installed, it may be enclosed with a water-tight wooden box, shown in Fig. 20B, in which case the space between the pipe and box is packed with sawdust, ground cork, mineral or other wool. The insulation between the pipe and the box

should not be less than 2 in. thick and it must be kept dry. A covering of roofing paper can be nailed over the box for this purpose. Sawdust makes good insulation but provides a good refuge for termites. It also settles after a while and more sawdust must be added occasionally to maintain its original thickness. Asphalt-impregnated fiber pipe, clay pipe, asbestos-cement and cement pipe can be used as an outside covering over insulation. An example of how an outside riser can be so protected is shown in Fig. 21. Underground piping should be laid below prevailing frost penetration. If this is not possible it should be covered with insulation protected against moisture.

Thawing frozen water pipes: Where electricity is available, the simplest method of thawing out a frozen pipe is by means of a pipe-thawing transformer such as used by many plumbers. While this method is quick, clean and relatively inexpensive, it is also hazardous if improperly done by novices. The clamps at the ends of two heavy cables are attached to the pipe on either side of the frozen section as shown in Fig. 22. An electric current flowing through the pipe between the clamps heats the pipe and melts the ice.

If such a pipe-thawing service is not available, and the frozen section of pipe is accessible, you can apply heat externally by holding an electric iron against the pipe or by placing an electric heater near it. However, when thawing a pipe by subjecting it to heat, never start at the middle of the

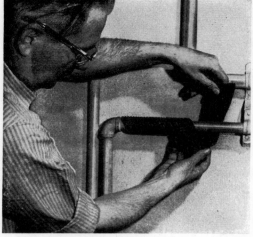

15

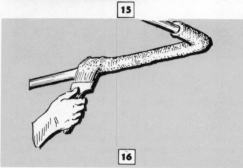

16

Laufenberg photo

17

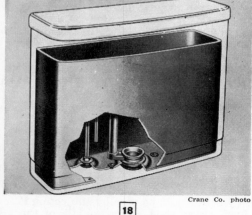

Crane Co. photo

18

frozen section since the expansion of heated water confined by ice, or possibly the formation of steam, may burst the pipe. Start thawing on the faucet side of the obstruction and work toward the supply, keeping the faucet open so that you will know when the ice has melted. Be ready, however, to turn off the water supply in case the pipe has been ruptured.

Heat can also be applied in other ways. About the simplest method is to wrap the pipe with twisted rags or burlap to obtain a suitable thickness, and then keep the wrapping saturated with boiling water, as in Fig. 23. A blowtorch will give quick results where the pipe is accessible and not close to wood, paper or other combustible material. A sheet of asbestos board also can be used as a protective shield. Another method is to run boiling water inside the pipe if part of the pipe can be removed as in Fig. 24, or if you can start working from an outlet. For horizontal pipes you run the boiling water through a small pipe so that it flows against the ice, and the cooled water drains off into a pail. In vertical lengths of pipe you can use a rubber tube in the same way, keeping its end against the ice. A jet of steam works still faster.

Scale and corrosion: Scale and corrosion on the inside of water pipes generally cause most damage to plumbing systems, since the pipes may become completely clogged. The rate at which scale and corrosion form varies with the chemical properties of the water and also its temperature. Scale forms faster on the rough surface of galvanized-iron pipe than it does on the smooth surface of brass pipe and copper tubing. It also forms faster wherever there is resistance to the flow of water as at elbows, tees and other fittings. Hard water causing scale formation can be recognized as such by its inability to form suds and lather easily. When hard water is artificially softened, the calcium and magnesium compounds which make it hard are removed.

Hard water is not as corrosive as natural soft water containing free carbon dioxide. A 40-deg. temperature rise in water about doubles its corrosive action and also hastens scale formation. Therefore, the life of hot-water pipes is considerably less than that of cold-water pipes. Rust "grows" to more than 10 times the volume of the iron from which it forms and this alone clogs pipes. Enough rust often is released in pipes to discolor the water and stain fabrics. Corrosiveness of water can be reduced considerably by removing the carbon-dioxide gas.

Clogged pipes and heater coils: When the flow of water from faucets becomes much less than it was when the pipes were new, the inside is probably caked with scale and corrosion. Replacement of the fittings alone may restore a satisfactory water flow for some time if the pipes themselves are not heavily coated. If badly caked, they should be replaced. Copper pipe and tubing are less subject to corrosion than iron and steel pipe; plastic pipe is not affected by corrosion but cannot be used for hot-water lines.

When it takes a long time for water to heat, the trouble may be caused by scale and corrosion accumulations in a heating coil or furnace water back in the pipes connecting these coils to hot-water tanks. The scale acts as insulation, preventing maximum heat transfer and consequently much time and heat are required to heat the water. As soon as such sluggish results are noticed in a coil water heater or water back, remove and inspect it. Generally badly caked coils and water backs must be replaced; although if the scale is caused by limestone, it can be softened and removed by using a muriatic-acid solution. This consists of muriatic acid, 1 part, slowly added and stirred into water, 4 to 7 parts, depending on the thickness of the scale. The mixing of the solution is done in a glass or porcelain container. Be careful not to get the acid on the skin or clothes as it causes burns and is corrosive and poisonous. To use the solution, close the lower opening of the coil, pour the solution into it and let it stand for a period of 4 to 6 hrs. Then pour out the solution and flush the coil with water to remove all traces of the acid. If one treatment does not remove the deposit, repeat as many times as is necessary. Deposits other than limestone, as for instance gypsum, are not appreciably affected by this solution. When a limestone-caked pipe is located in a wall or other place where it cannot be removed easily for replacement without considerable damage, the acid treatment can be tried.

Frost precautions in closed house: When a house is closed during cold weather and is not heated, the water system must be drained completely to prevent damage from freezing. First shut off the water supply at the main control valve near the meter, and turn off the heat source of the water heater. Then open the drain valve at the lowest point of the piping and also open all faucets so that water will flow out more easily. Also open the drain faucet on the water heater, and if it has a heat trap, water must be removed from this also. For this reason a drain valve should be provided at the lower point of the trap. Empty water-closet tanks by flushing. If the system includes water-softening or conditioning equipment, or any tanks for water storage, these too must be emptied completely. It also is advisable to have the water service turned off at the curb valve and to have the water

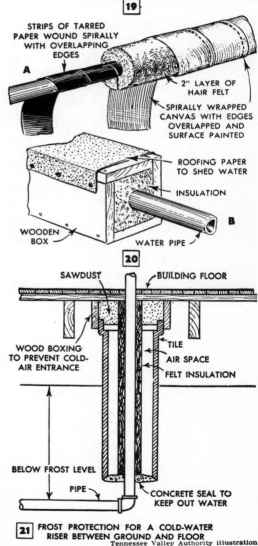

STRIPS OF TARRED PAPER WOUND SPIRALLY WITH OVERLAPPING EDGES

A

2" LAYER OF HAIR FELT

SPIRALLY WRAPPED CANVAS WITH EDGES OVERLAPPED AND SURFACE PAINTED

ROOFING PAPER TO SHED WATER

INSULATION

WOODEN BOX

WATER PIPE

B

SAWDUST

BUILDING FLOOR

WOOD BOXING TO PREVENT COLD-AIR ENTRANCE

TILE

AIR SPACE

FELT INSULATION

BELOW FROST LEVEL

PIPE

CONCRETE SEAL TO KEEP OUT WATER

21 FROST PROTECTION FOR A COLD-WATER RISER BETWEEN GROUND AND FLOOR

Tennessee Valley Authority illustration

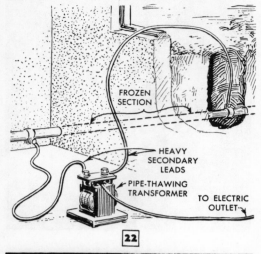

FROZEN SECTION

HEAVY SECONDARY LEADS

PIPE-THAWING TRANSFORMER

TO ELECTRIC OUTLET

22

23

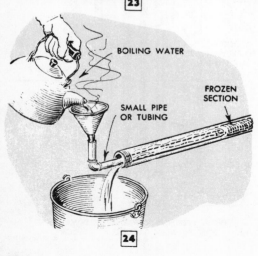

BOILING WATER

SMALL PIPE OR TUBING

FROZEN SECTION

24

meter removed. If this is not done the exposed part of the service pipe and meter should be carefully insulated to prevent water inside from freezing. Water in heating systems and traps of the drainage system, including water-closet traps, must be removed also. Kerosene is substituted for water in traps.

Water-pressure troubles: One of the most common complaints of home water supplies is variation of water pressure; for example, a running mixture of hot and cold water at a shower or bath suddenly varies in volume of flow and temperature due to drawing water from another outlet. Such variations often are enough to cause discomforts and may even result in injury when the water mixture becomes scalding. Where such trouble is constant and frequent, the water pipes may be too small—either of inadequate diameter for their length and height as originally installed, or their diameter may have been reduced by liming and corrosion. Another cause of inadequate pressure and water flow is excessive friction in the pipe due to too many fittings and changes of direction. Or, piping originally adequate may have become overloaded by an extra bathroom or automatic washing equipment.

When variations of pressure at shower and bath outlets only occur when other outlets are opened, the situation can be remedied usually by installing automatic mixing valves. This, however, does not increase the maximum water flow from an inadequately sized pipe, which can be done only by replacing the pipe with one of larger size. Replacement of pipe also becomes necessary where water pressure is inadequate at outlets but is sufficient at the service-line entrance.

Temporary low pressure can be occasioned by large amounts of water being drawn off the city mains in the neighborhood, as for instance by fire equipment, but this trouble is only temporary. A pressure gauge at the meter location will show whether continued low pressure at outlets is caused by pipe resistance inside of the house or whether the fault lies outside. It can be occasioned by a service pipe that is clogged or is of too small diameter. This is likely to be the case if the pressure at the curb valve is much higher than that at the house entrance of the service pipe. A clogged service pipe can be cleared by using a drain auger (new or sterilized). When pressure at the curb valve is not much higher than that of the house end of the service line, the fault may be an obstruction between the curb valve and the city water main, or the pressure of the latter may be insufficient. Where water pressures are too high, which may cause water hammer and

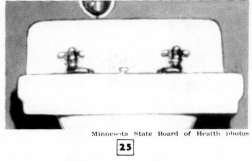

Minnesota State Board of Health photos

25

26

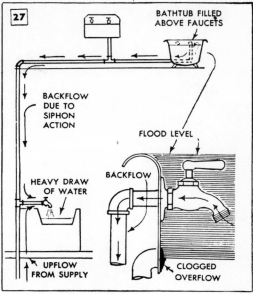

whistling noises, the pressure can be reduced by using a pressure-reducing valve. Where water pressures are too low in water lines, a condition may be created where backflow from fixtures is experienced, as described below.

Hazards of cross connections and backflow: Polluted water from a drainage system may get into the water-supply lines under certain conditions. This has caused numerous epidemics such as the amoebic dysentery in Chicago during 1933. Amoebic dysentery is most common in warm or tropical countries, but it may break out in cooler climates as evidenced by the Chicago epidemic. Germs causing typhoid fever and other diseases, once inside the water pipes, can spread to all parts of the system. Chlorinated water used in many cities kills all known waterborne germs except the one causing amoebic dysentery; this one is able to survive about 15 days in chlorinated water. The disease can sometimes be cured by the use of drugs, but prevention is the best cure.

When a water-supply outlet is located below the flood-level rim of a fixture, the outlet will be submerged when the fixture is filled. Then a cross connection exists between the drainage and the water-supply lines. This is especially likely to occur with obsolete fixtures such as shown in Figs. 25 and 26. When a water-supply outlet is submerged, the contents of drainage lines can be sucked into the water line. This happens when pressure in the water line is decreased below atmospheric pressure and

may be occasioned when a large quantity of water is drawn off at a lower point in the house as illustrated in Fig. 27. The polluted water can even seep through a closed faucet if it is leaky, or it can be drawn up through a spray nozzle submerged in a bathtub or kitchen sink. This reverse flow is called back-siphonage or backflow. It is especially likely to occur when a lower water-supply branch is much larger than necessary. It can also be caused by a broken water main or a heavy draw from the water main by fire apparatus. Draining water from a basement or first-floor outlet while the main supply line is shut off causes backflow from points above.

Backflow is particularly common in downfeed water systems—those having an overhead supply tank from which water flows down to fixtures. It can occur also in any upfeed system—water supplied from city main or pressure tank below fixtures.

Preventing cross connections: Cross connections and backflow can be eliminated as follows: (1) by providing a suitable air gap between the outlet and the flood-level rim of a fixture (where this is impossible an approved type of backflow preventer or vacuum breaker should be used), and (2) by assuring a positive water pressure at all outlets at all times.

Air gaps should not be less than 1 in. for a lavatory, 1½ in. for a kitchen sink or laundry tub, and 2 in. for a bathtub. If outlets are closer to a vertical wall than twice these distances, the normal air gap in each case should be increased 50 percent. Old fixtures often can be altered to meet these requirements.

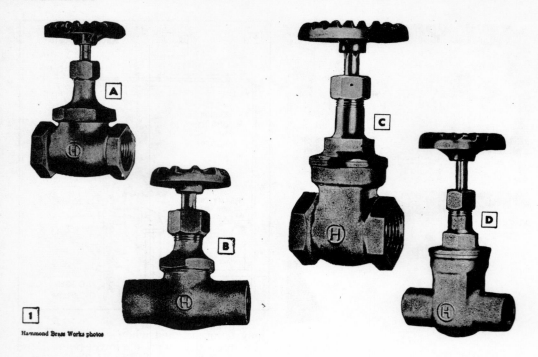

Hammond Brass Works photos

Valves and Faucets

CONTROL OF WATER SUPPLY is the function of valves and faucets, which also are referred to as cocks, bibbs, stops and taps. Valves and sill cocks are used on pipe lines; faucets are installed at fixtures. Having a sufficient number of valves in a water system enables you to shut off any branch individually instead of the entire system. Being able to do so quickly may prevent flooding and costly repairs. Valves in home plumbing lines usually are cast bronze and have portions machined and threaded for trimmings. See details A and C of Fig. 1. The port ends (ends that connect to lines) may be tapped for screwing to pipe or may be smooth for soldered joints to tubing as in details B and D. Since valves are of different types for specific purposes, they should be installed accordingly.

Gate valves: A gate valve, of which a cross-sectional view is shown in Fig. 2, has a sliding wedge that is moved across the waterway, usually by means of a threaded spindle or stem. This may be the rising or the nonrising type; the latter type has the shorter bonnet. A gate valve is primarily used to completely shut off or completely open a waterway, but not to control the volume of flow. Either port (opening) of a gate valve may face the pressure side of

the line. The chief advantage of a gate valve is that it permits complete passage of water without adding appreciable resistance to the flow. Therefore gate valves should be used on all supply lines that are in constant use, particularly where water pressure is low.

The sliding wedge or gate may be either solid or split, as in details A and B of Fig. 3. One part of a split wedge pivots on a rounded seat on the other so that they automatically adjust themselves to the angle of the double seat. The seat may be part of the body casting ground to a smooth surface, or it may have inserted corrosion-resistant rings. The waterway through the seat corresponds in size to the size of pipe on which the valve fits. Often the bonnet that holds the spindle in place is attached to the body with a union ring. The spindle may be either the stationary or the traveling type. When leakage develops between disk and seat, it is generally necessary to replace the valve because it is difficult to reface the seat, although new disks may be installed.

Globe and angle valves: Wherever a valve must be opened and closed frequently, and water pressure is sufficiently high, a globe valve, Fig. 4, is customarily used in spite of the added resistance it introduces into the line. Globe valves also are generally used to control volume of flow. A globe valve has two chambers. The partition between them is drilled for the passage of water, which must change its course several times from port to port, Fig. 5A, introducing resistance. Therefore, globe valves generally should not be used in water-supply lines to serve occasional shut-off purposes only. To close a globe valve, a disk, usually faced with a composition washer, is brought down on the seat by turning the spindle. The ground seat may be flat or beveled as in detail B of Fig. 5.

Often globe valves are installed so that the water pressure is exerted under the disk. When so installed, spindle packing can be replaced while the valve is closed—or when fully opened if it has a back seat that prevents leakage of water past the spindle. When a globe valve having no back seat is installed so that water pressure is exerted downward, the supply line must be shut off for packing the stem. However, downward pressure on the disk minimizes trouble from leakage, tends to keep the valve closed when not tightly shut off by hand, and in case of failure of threads on the spindle, the valve will close automatically instead of "blowing open." When a globe valve is installed on horizontal pipe so that the handle sets vertically either above or below the valve, water will not drain out of the line completely, as indicated in detail C. To avoid this trouble, arrange the spindle horizontally so that water can pass through the seat opening as in detail D.

An angle valve is similar to a globe valve but has its ports at right angles, Fig. 6. Usually the water passage is larger than it is on a globe valve, and since there is only one change of direction of flow, less resistance is introduced. An angle valve installed at a turn in piping eliminates the need of an elbow, and often is preferable to using a globe valve and an elbow.

Reconditioning globe and angle valves: Most globe and angle valves have a composition washer which should be replaced at the first sign of leakage. After removing the spindle assembly, loosen the screw or nut holding the washer. Remove the washer and carefully scrape away all traces of it that may have stuck to the disk, Fig. 7. The new washer, held either by a screw or nut, should be tightened in place securely. If a nut is used to hold the washer, it is prick-punched to lock it on the projecting threaded end. For valves on hot-water lines, use only the hard or semihard washers. The semihard washers are also used on cold-water lines, but the soft, resilient type is preferable. Washers come in various diameters and should be selected to fit the washer holder accurately.

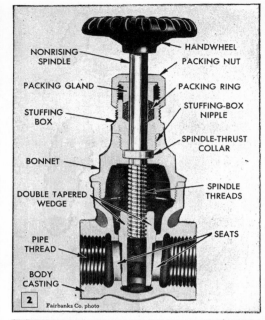

NONRISING SPINDLE
HANDWHEEL
PACKING NUT
PACKING GLAND
PACKING RING
STUFFING BOX
STUFFING-BOX NIPPLE
SPINDLE-THRUST COLLAR
BONNET
SPINDLE THREADS
DOUBLE TAPERED WEDGE
SEATS
PIPE THREAD
BODY CASTING

2 Fairbanks Co. photo

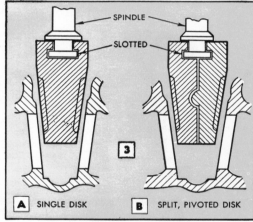

SPINDLE
SLOTTED

3

A SINGLE DISK   **B** SPLIT, PIVOTED DISK

When a new washer does not produce a tight seal, the valve seat requires dressing. Some globe valves have renewable seat inserts. To dress the seat of a small globe or angle valve, you use a standard reseating tool of the kind shown in Fig. 26, which also is used for reseating compression faucets. Use very slight pressure on the reseating tool and remove only as much metal as is necessary to obtain a smooth seat. When finished, remove the chips before reassembling. If a valve seat has been weakened by repeated dressing, or is damaged beyond repair, a seat insert, Fig. 27, is less expensive than replacing the valve. However, as the insert restricts the opening, it should be used only if water pressure is adequate.

Globe and angle valves not fitted with composition washers, but having a metal-

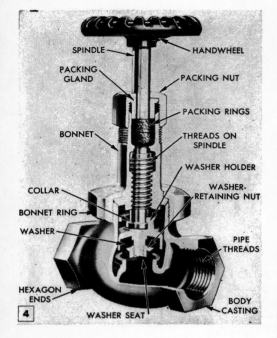

Figure 4 labels:
- SPINDLE
- HANDWHEEL
- PACKING GLAND
- PACKING NUT
- PACKING RINGS
- BONNET
- THREADS ON SPINDLE
- WASHER HOLDER
- WASHER-RETAINING NUT
- COLLAR
- BONNET RING
- WASHER
- PIPE THREADS
- HEXAGON ENDS
- BODY CASTING
- WASHER SEAT

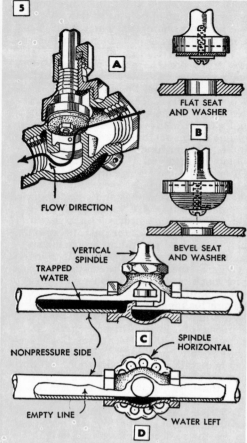

FLOW DIRECTION
FLAT SEAT AND WASHER
BEVEL SEAT AND WASHER
VERTICAL SPINDLE
TRAPPED WATER
NONPRESSURE SIDE
SPINDLE HORIZONTAL
EMPTY LINE
WATER LEFT

ANGLE VALVE
Fairbanks Co. photos

SCRAPE OFF TRACES OF OLD WASHER

TIGHTEN SCREW ON WASHER

to-metal seat contact, are sometimes preferred for hot-water lines. Leaky seats of this kind must be reground. Some valves have provision for locking the disk to the spindle, such as a grooved locknut and a small hole in the spindle for a holding pin, permitting the spindle to be used as a grinding tool. After locking the disk to the spindle and putting a moderate amount of grinding compound between disk and seat, screw down the union ring tightly with the fingers but then back it up exactly one full turn to keep the spindle perfectly vertical. More than this would allow the spindle to be tilted while grinding. To grind, turn the spindle back and forth not more than a quarter turn, a number of times at different points of contact between disk and seat. Do not overgrind. Clean out the grinding compound thoroughly before reassembling.

Plug or key valves: These, shown in Fig. 8, have a tapered, ground plug fitting a mating tapered hole or seat. An opening through the plug provides an unobstructed waterway producing minimum resistance to flow. In this respect, it is comparable to a gate valve. A quarter turn opens and closes the valve. The common type shown

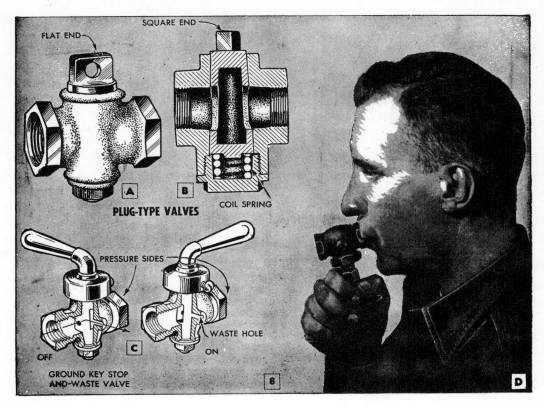

FLAT END

SQUARE END

COIL SPRING

PLUG-TYPE VALVES

A B

PRESSURE SIDES

WASTE HOLE

OFF C ON

GROUND KEY STOP
AND-WASTE VALVE

8

D

in detail A has both ends of the plug extending outside of the body. The large end may be flat, or square so as to take a small wrench, or it may be provided with a handle as in detail C. The small end usually is threaded for a nut which holds the plug snugly in its seat. On the type shown in detail B the arrangement is reversed; the small end is the handle end and the large end is placed under pressure of a coil spring. This type generally causes less leakage. Because of the spring there is less danger of distorting the plug in case the water is frozen.

In a plug valve, sand or grit in the water is likely to jam or scratch the ground surfaces, resulting in leakage. Therefore, these valves are not durable when subjected to constant use, but are very serviceable for occasional shut-off purposes. They often are required by code as a main shut-off valve on the street side of a meter, in which case they should be of the drainable type. The same kind also may be used on lines supplying sill cocks where globe valves introduce too much resistance to flow. Curb stops are usually of this type also. When leaky, such valves must be replaced as a rule. Sometimes it is possible to recondition them by using valve-grinding compound, but it is difficult to restore the original mating surfaces.

Drainable valves: Valves, which are provided with a small drain outlet in the body to allow water in the nonpressure side of the line to be drained out when the valve is closed, are called drainable or stop-and-waste valves. Gate, globe and plug valves can be of this type. Detail C of Fig. 8 shows a drainable plug valve. To determine which port should face the line pressure, you blow into both ports as shown in detail D while the valve is closed and the drain outlet is open. The port through which air flows is the one to connect to the line requiring drainage.

Installing valves: Be sure to cut pipe threads to the correct length (so the pipe end comes to the edge of the die). If the threaded end is too long, the pipe can be forced against the diaphragm or seat of a valve, which may distort it. Avoid excess pipe dope and don't put it on the internal threads of a valve. Support pipe adequately to prevent strain on valves, especially small ones. Before installing a valve be sure that the pipe has been cleaned thoroughly of chips caused by threading and reaming, and also of other foreign matter. This may lodge on the valve seat and cause trouble. Open the valve and clean it out thoroughly by flushing with water. After cleaning, close the valve and then install it. Use a flat-jaw wrench that fits the hexagon parts.

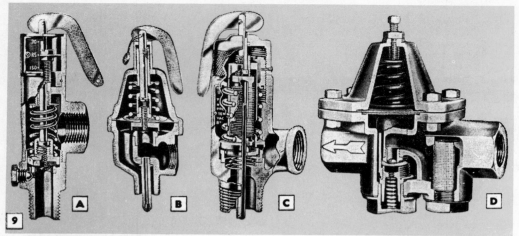

A. W. Cash Valve Mfg. Co. photos

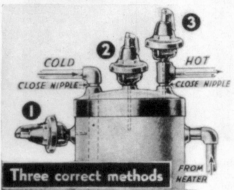

Three correct methods

Valve maintenance: A very slight leakage of water, especially hot water, across the seat of a valve wears tiny grooves in it. This is known as "wire-drawing" and eventually damages a valve beyond repair. When a valve cannot be closed tightly by hand, don't use a wrench or apply any other form of leverage to force it tighter as this may ruin it. Inspect valves periodically. When a valve is shut and water continues to trickle from an outlet under its control, the valve leaks. The remedy depends on its type and condition.

When water leaks from the stem or spindle, the packing must be replaced. To do this, loosen the packing nut, lift up the gland, remove the old packing and replace it Use graphited asbestos packing. The split-ring type of correct size is most convenient but a few turns of the stranded type of wicking also is effective. When replacing the packing nut don't turn it too tight; just tight enough so that the packing will stop leakage. Some valves have a "back seat" which allows them to be opened fully when repacking the stuffing box. Others require turning off the water.

Safety-relief valves for water heaters: A safety-relief valve on a hot-water tank opens to let out water at a predetermined pressure and temperature below the danger point. There are two basic types of relief valves: the pop-type valve, and the diaphragm-type valve. Both are shown in details A and B of Fig. 9. Both kinds are spring-loaded, and are either preset by the manufacturer to release at a certain pressure or are adjustable to various pressures like the one shown in detail A, which also has a visual pressure scale that can be turned to any convenient position. Both types of valves are obtainable with fusible plugs which melt at a temperature of 210 or 212 deg. F., allowing hot water to escape and cold water to enter the tank, until the water is shut off and another plug inserted. A fusible plug in the side of the valve, as shown in detail A, can be replaced without unscrewing the valve, which is necessary when replacing a plug fitted on the end of a stem as shown in detail B. The latter kind, however, are more critical. The need of replacing a fusible plug calls definite attention to a possible disorder.

Another type of relief valve, shown in detail C, is opened and closed automatically by either pressure or temperature. In addition to a spring-loaded pressure release, this type has a thermostatic bellows, to which a short or long stem is connected. It comes either with or without a test lever. Such valves with short stems are used for ordinary water heaters and those having long stems are recommended for electric heaters and insulated tanks.

A valve that relieves pressure only, and is not provided with a temperature-actuated relief feature, may stick and fail to function when necessary. It is also desirable to have a relief valve fitted with a test lever used occasionally to check the working condition of the valve. Selection of a relief valve must be made so that it conforms to local code requirements. A relief valve should be installed at the point of maximum water temperature, not more than 3 in. from the tank. It is installed usually with a T-fitting at the hot-water connection to the tank but it may be located at other positions. See Fig. 10. No other valve should be placed between the relief valve and the tank. Relief valves are especially important on "closed" water systems — those fitted with check valves or pressure-reducing valves.

Pressure-reducing valves: Wherever water pressure exceeds 80 or 90 p.s.i., a pressure-reducing and regulating valve should be installed in the water line near the meter and in an accessible position. Its purpose is to minimize or eliminate "water hammer," which causes annoying noise and also subjects pipes, valves, faucets and even fixtures to severe strains which may damage them. Detail D of Fig. 9 shows a cutaway view of one type of pressure regulator designed for domestic use. Standard factory practice is to preset such valves to maintain a uniform outlet pressure of about 45 p.s.i., but other reduced pressure settings are available. Specifications necessary for selecting the right size of valve are maximum inlet pressure, required delivery pressure and capacity of the water system in gal. or cu. ft. per minute. Seats of these valves usually are renewable, and some types are provided with a strainer on the inlet side, which requires occasional cleaning. Wherever a pressure regulator is used it is essential to provide a pressure-relief valve on the low-pressure side of the line, as accomplished with a safety-relief valve on a water heater.

Check valves: Fig. 11 shows a solder-end, swing-type check valve and Fig. 12 shows the inside of a similar valve having pipe-thread ends. A check valve operates automatically, permitting flow in one direction only. Sometimes a check valve is combined with a throttling or shut-off valve. Some localities require a check valve in a cold-water line between the water heater and the meter. Also, check valves are used to prevent water pumped to an overhead tank from flowing back when the pump stops. Some check valves are designed for use on vertical pipes only; others are for horizontal pipes only. Therefore correct installation is essential. The closing device—disk, ball or clapper—should fall shut by gravity.

Swing-type check valves generally used in horizontal water-supply lines are installed so that the small projections on the outside of the body will be nearest the pressure side of the line; the cap that closes the body should face up. If a composition washer is used on the disk, it can be renewed

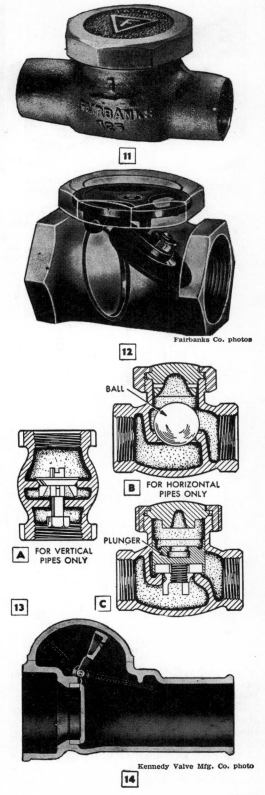

11

Fairbanks Co. photos

12

BALL

B FOR HORIZONTAL PIPES ONLY

PLUNGER

A FOR VERTICAL PIPES ONLY

13

C

Kennedy Valve Mfg. Co. photo

14

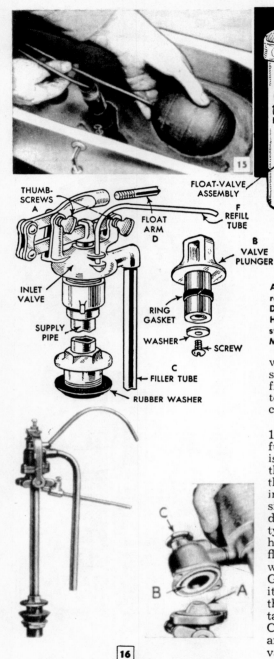

THUMB-
SCREWS
A

FLOAT-VALVE
ASSEMBLY

FLOAT
ARM
D

F
REFILL
TUBE

B
VALVE
PLUNGER

INLET
VALVE

RING
GASKET

SUPPLY
PIPE

WASHER

SCREW

C
FILLER TUBE

RUBBER WASHER

WATER
SUPPLY

WATER
LEVEL

M

FLUSH
VALVE

Above and at the left: A, pins or thumbscrews to release valve plunger; B, valve plunger; C, filler tube; D, float arm; E, float; F, refill tube; G, overflow pipe; H, trip-lever handle; I, trip lever to release rubber stopper; J and L, stopper wires; K, stopper guide; M, stopper; N, flush-valve seat; O, discharge pipe

water," or "backflow," valve. These are installed in house drains to prevent sewage from backing up into them. Information as to location and method of installation is contained in the section on *Drainage*.

Valves on tank-type water closets: Fig. 15 shows a water-closet flush tank which functions by means of two valves. One is a float-controlled valve (float valve) through which water enters. The other is the discharge valve. Different makes vary in detail but the operating principles are similar. When the float E is raised to a predetermined level, the valve closes. On some types an adjustment screw controls float height, which is preferable to bending float-arm D, necessary in other types. When water continues to run into overflow pipe G, the float valve is not fully closed or else it leaks. Reason for not closing may be that the float rubs against the tank wall or contains some water caused by pinhole leaks. Check the valve action by raising the float arm to shut it. If water still escapes, the valve is leaky.

The usual repair consists of renewing the washer on plunger B, which is removed by loosening thumbscrews A, after turning off the water supply. The washer may be different from the one illustrated, or it may be a disk held by a brass ring. Sometimes the valve seat can be refaced, using the same method as for faucets. If reconditioning the valve does not stop leakage, replace it. Float valves come in either short or long lengths. Sometimes the threaded tailpiece.

when leakage develops. On valves not so equipped it may be necessary to replace the valve. On lift-type check valves, details A, B and C of Fig. 13, the line pressure should be under the seat. When leaky, these valves can sometimes be reground like globe valves. Others require renewal of the disk and seat, or must be replaced entirely. Fig. 14 shows a swing-type check valve of much larger size—called a "back-

held in place on the tank bottom with lock-nuts and rubber washers, need not be removed if the supply pipe can be screwed into it. Filler tube C, also called the "hush tube," extends almost to the bottom of the tank so that the end will be submerged while refilling the tank. This reduces noise by eliminating splashing.

The water level in a tank should not extend above the float valve as this causes a cross connection. It is always best to have a float valve fitted with a backflow preventer or vacuum breaker. As little as 4 gal. of water will flush a bowl generally, but most tanks discharge more than this. Excess water serves no useful purpose and is merely wasted. If the water level is too high, adjust the float. Saving 2 or 3 qts. of water at each flushing means a considerable total in a year. The refill tube F empties into the overflow pipe G and supplies water to seal the bowl trap after flushing.

Leakage from tank to bowl through the discharge valve is quite frequent. This may be caused by grit on the plastic or rubber stopper M, by its being worn, by not seating properly, or by grit or corrosion on the stopper seat N. Improper seating may result if stopper guide K, clamped to overflow pipe G, is not concentric with the stopper seat. Wire L, which screws to a stopper, should project about 1 in. through the eye on the end of wire J, which connects to the trip lever I. If this alignment and the action of stopper seem to be correct, remove the stopper by unscrewing it from the wire, and clean the rounded surface. Also dry valve seat N and clean it with fine emery cloth. If the valve still continues to leak, substitute a new stopper. Usually stoppers require replacement every few years. If the valve seat is badly corroded, replace the seat and overflow unit.

The type of float valve shown in Fig. 16 is designed to give quiet action. Valve seat A is vitreous china, which resists the corrosive effects of water. Adjustment C controls flow at B for minimum noise.

Flush valves on water closets: Flush-valve operated water closets are connected

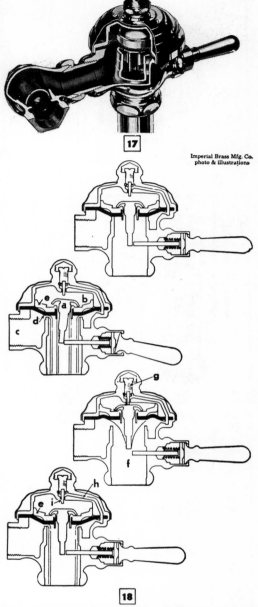

Imperial Brass Mfg. Co.
photo & illustrations

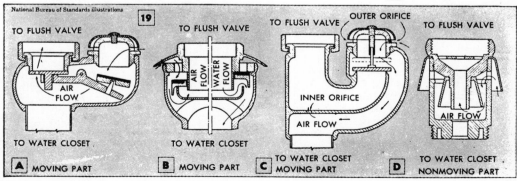

National Bureau of Standards illustrations

TO FLUSH VALVE — AIR FLOW — TO WATER CLOSET — **A** MOVING PART

TO FLUSH VALVE — AIR FLOW — WATER FLOW — TO WATER CLOSET — **B** MOVING PART

TO FLUSH VALVE — OUTER ORIFICE — INNER ORIFICE — AIR FLOW — TO WATER CLOSET — **C** MOVING PART

TO FLUSH VALVE — AIR FLOW — TO WATER CLOSET — **D** NONMOVING PART

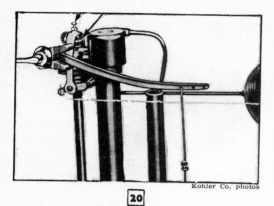

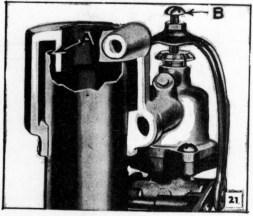

20

Kohler Co. photos

21

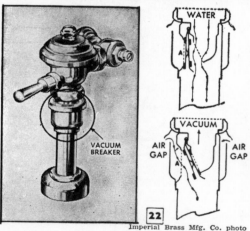

VACUUM
BREAKER

WATER

A

VACUUM

AIR
GAP

AIR
GAP

A

22

Imperial Brass Mfg. Co. photo

water closet. The rate of flow on flush valves is often adjustable.

Flush valves use less water than flush tanks and can be operated at intervals of only a few seconds. They also take less space and generally require less servicing than the mechanism in a tank-type water closet. There are several types of flush valves, including the diaphragm, piston and plunger types. Fig. 17 shows a cutaway view of a diaphragm-type flush valve. The four views of Fig. 18 show how it operates. At the start of a flush, the handle tilts valve "a," relieving pressure in upper chamber "b," and allowing water pressure in supply pipe "c" to exert force upwards on diaphragm "d," raising main unit "e" so that maximum flow of water passes through outlet "f." Raised valve "a" pressing against the plunger on regulating screw "g," widens opening "i" to momentarily increase flow of water through bypass "h," cleaning it and filling chamber, which forces main unit down to starting position.

Backflow preventers: Fig. 19 shows four types of backflow preventers or vacuum breakers. Those in details A, B and C have moving parts, while the one in detail D has nonmoving parts. Backflow preventers are used where it is not possible to have an air gap between the water-supply outlet and the flood-level rim of a fixture. This is explained in *Water System Troubles*. A backflow preventer is placed between a control valve and the fixture. Moving parts, such as a pivoted or sliding disk, are permitted on acceptable types of backflow preventers, but they cannot include springs or other elastic or flexible parts.

The backflow preventer shown in Figs. 20 and 21 is an atmospheric type and is combined with a water-closet float valve. "A" indicates where air enters and "B" is the adjustment screw to vary height of float valve so the water level will be 1 in. below the top of the overflow tube. All flush-valve water closets should be equipped with backflow preventers installed as in Fig. 22, which also shows the working principle of this design.

Compression faucets and sill cocks: Various styles of single and combination faucets are shown in Fig. 23. Some are connected to a common spout. Practically all modern faucets are of the compression type. Fig. 24 shows the working parts of a faucet. Notice its similarity to a globe valve. A drilled partition forms a seat against which a composition washer is brought down by a threaded spindle.

Continued dripping of water after a faucet has been tightly closed by hand usually indicates a worn washer. To repair it first shut off the water supply. Then loosen the cap nut on the faucet with a flat-jaw

directly to the water-supply line, which generally should not be less than 1 in., although ¾-in. pipe may be satisfactory for unusually high pressures. Flush valves require from 10 to 20 lbs. per sq. in. (p.s.i.) pressure. This varies with units due to the differences in design. The discharge capacity also varies with design from 20 to 40 g.p.m., but the duration of discharge is so short that the total volume of water used is less than that discharged by a tank-type

wrench. Protect the chrome or nickel finish from being marred by inserting a strip of cardboard between the nut and the wrench jaws. If the cap nut is round and the edges are grooved, use a strap wrench. After loosening the cap nut, turn the faucet handle in counter-clockwise direction so that the threaded spindle unscrews. Then you can lift out the spindle assembly as in detail A of Fig. 25. It may be necessary also to turn the faucet handle at the same time to provide clearance for the nut. Next, loosen the brass screw that holds the old washer on the end of the spindle, detail B. Sometimes the screw is corroded and is so tight that it will not loosen readily. An application of penetrating oil may help. If the screw breaks off, it usually can be removed by drilling a small hole in the remaining threaded portion, and turning out the remaining shell of the screw with the tang end of a small file. If necessary, scrape away all traces of the old washer. To determine the size of a new one, measure the diameter of the recess in which it fits as in detail C. It is sometimes necessary to dress the outside edge of a washer with a file to make it slip into the washer holder.

With the new washer in place, turn the spindle into the faucet and then screw the cap nut down. If necessary, the faucet handle can be shifted as in detail D after removing the screw holding it. Some faucets, however, have handles that cannot be removed from the spindles. For example, there is one in which the spindle works in a sleeve which is lifted out with the spindle. The spindle washer moves upward against the bottom of the sleeve when closing. Replacement of the washer is practically the same, except that a nut holds the washer instead of a screw.

Refacing faucet seats: If the flat surface of the faucet seat against which the washer compresses is rough, it will be impossible to prevent recurring leaks by merely installing new washers. Such roughness is caused by corrosion or by abrasion due to sand and grit particles becoming embedded in the washer. The roughened seat should

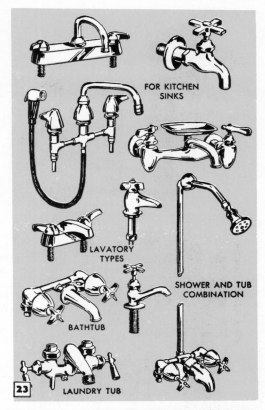

23 FOR KITCHEN SINKS — LAVATORY TYPES — SHOWER AND TUB COMBINATION — BATHTUB — LAUNDRY TUB

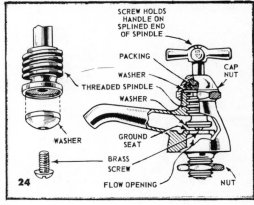

24 SCREW HOLDS HANDLE ON SPLINED END OF SPINDLE — PACKING — WASHER — THREADED SPINDLE — WASHER — CAP NUT — GROUND SEAT — BRASS SCREW — FLOW OPENING — NUT — WASHER

25

A Lift out the spindle

B Remove the washer

C Measure washer size

D Adjust faucet handle

26

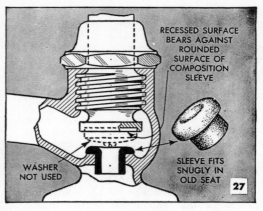

RECESSED SURFACE BEARS AGAINST ROUNDED SURFACE OF COMPOSITION SLEEVE

WASHER NOT USED

SLEEVE FITS SNUGLY IN OLD SEAT

27

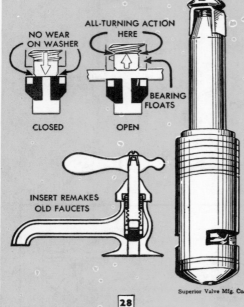

NO WEAR ON WASHER

ALL-TURNING ACTION HERE

BEARING FLOATS

CLOSED

OPEN

INSERT REMAKES OLD FAUCETS

Superior Valve Mfg. Co.

28

29

inside the old seat as in Fig. 27. The washer and screw are removed permanently from the end of the spindle, which then bears against the sleeve insert when the faucet is closed.

The process of reseating or refacing leaky faucets or replacing old faucets can be avoided generally by using a faucet insert of the kind shown in Fig. 28. When this insert is used it is not necessary to remove the faucet from the pipe. It provides a new stem, new seat and new threads. It has a nonturn compression shut-off (floating bronze bearing), which is held tightly against a rubber washer by the threaded spindle when the faucet is turned off. Turning the faucet on permits water pressure to force the bearing up. The washer is held in the end of the shell of the unit and does not rotate. The lower surface of the washer is held tightly against the faucet seat by the pressure exerted by the cap nut on the upper end of the shell. As the bearing simply presses down against the washer there is no rotary movement that causes the washer to wear. Water passes through two ports in the shell when the bearing is raised. The insert fits nearly all faucets. To install one, the cap nut of the faucet is unscrewed, the old faucet stem is removed, the insert put in place and the cap nut and handle are replaced.

Leaky spindle: Leaks sometimes develop between the spindle and the cap nut of a faucet. If tightening of the cap nut does not stop the leak, loosen the nut, slip it up against the handle and replace the packing. Sometimes it is necessary to remove the nut from the spindle entirely in order to remove the old packing. You can use a packing washer of correct size, or stranded graphite-asbestos wicking, which is wrapped around the spindle as in Fig. 29.

Repairing Fuller faucets: Although practically obsolete, there are still many Fuller faucets in older homes. On this type, shown in Fig. 30, the handle can be swung in either direction to open or close the faucet. A hor-

be refaced by means of the tool shown in Fig. 26. Care must be taken to hold the refacing tool vertically and to use light pressure. After refacing the seat, see that all bits of metal are flushed away before replacing the faucet spindle. Another method of providing a new seat, which eliminates the cost of a refacing tool, is to use a special composition sleeve that is pressed

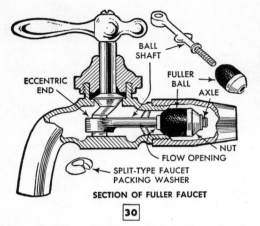

SECTION OF FULLER FAUCET

30

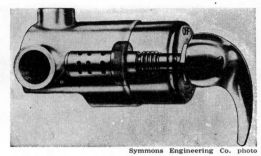

Symmons Engineering Co. photo

31

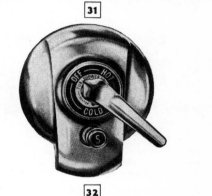

32

FROSTPROOF HYDRANT

33

izontal spindle with an acorn-shaped rubber stopper or ball (Fuller ball) at one end is moved back and forth by means of a crank-shaped vertical spindle to which the handle is attached. The entire faucet must be removed when the ball is adjusted or replaced. The sleeve enclosing the ball is unscrewed if the nut that holds the ball cannot be reached with a long-nose pliers. Turning the nut to bring the ball closer to the seat may stop the leak, or a new ball may be required. A worn spindle or ball shaft can be replaced at small cost.

Mixing faucets: Combination faucets to mix hot and cold water are in common use for kitchen sinks, lavatories, laundry tubs, bathtubs and showers. They cannot be depended on to keep the water at a uniform temperature. For example, when water is drawn from another outlet while a shower is being used, the temperature of the shower water may fluctuate widely because of the reduced pressure. This may result in an extremely cold or in a scalding mixture, with possible serious consequences.

Automatic mixing valves for showers: Temperature of shower water can be maintained within a few degrees even when there are pressure drops of as much as 90 percent in either hot or cold-water line. This is accomplished by means of a pressure-controlled mixing valve such as shown in Fig. 31. Fig. 32 shows the exposed portion of a slightly different model having a control valve that directs water to either shower or bath. The mixer consists of a cylinder containing a free-moving, pressure-equalizing piston. The latter is actuated by cold-water pressure at one end and hot-water pressure at the other, which directly controls the amount of hot and cold water admitted and so maintains the temperature of the mixed water as originally adjusted. The interior of the valve is completely accessible from the front for replacing washers or the seat unit, should this become necessary. The valve shown is

the concealed model with only the handle and front plate visible. Exposed models also are available. Thermostatically controlled mixing valves also are available.

Frost-proof hydrants: Where an outdoor outlet is connected to an underground supply pipe and is used the year around in localities where the outlet is likely to be damaged by frost, a frost-proof hydrant, Fig. 33, has the great advantage of being trouble-free. The valve is located below frost level and is operated by an extension rod. When closed, the valve drains off water from the riser pipe. A gravel or sand bed, as indicated, permits rapid dissipation of the drained water. Insulating the riser pipe helps to prevent ice formation inside.

1753

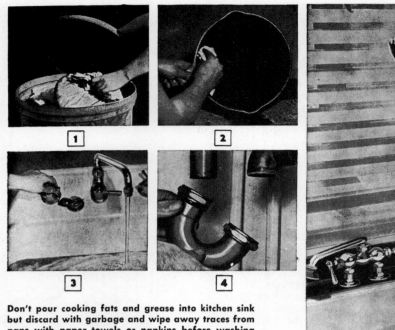

Don't pour cooking fats and grease into kitchen sink but discard with garbage and wipe away traces from pans with paper towels or napkins before washing

Flush sink drain with scalding-hot water for 2 or 3 minutes each day. When waste pipe is clogged, remove trap so drain auger can be easily advanced to obstruction

Drainage Troubles-Causes and Cures

AMONG TROUBLES EXPERIENCED in drainage systems, the most common ones are clogging of pipes, especially those from kitchen sinks; root penetration into house sewers; backflow of sewage into house drains and the entrance of sewer gas into houses. Less common are freezing of drainage lines, leaky pipes and drainage-system noises. Some of these troubles can be remedied easily by most homeowners; others are more involved but can also be done by homeowners at a considerable saving in cost. In any case the problem encountered becomes much easier to solve when you can diagnose it correctly, locate its source and know where and how to apply an effective remedy. Besides curing an existing trouble, measures should be taken in order to prevent its recurrence.

Clogged sink drains: Most stoppages in kitchen-sink waste lines are caused by accumulations of congealed grease and fat emptied into the sink. Coffee grounds, food particles and lint are held in this grease deposit which gradually builds up until it obstructs the pipe completely. Generally the trouble occurs in a horizontal portion of the waste pipe. Therefore this part should always be provided with an accessible cleanout, shown in Fig. 8.

Too steep a slope in this section also causes the water to drain away fast which is apt to leave solids stranded in the pipe which will obstruct it. If part of a sink-waste pipe is enclosed in an outside wall, as in Fig. 8, grease is likely to congeal here. Clogging seldom starts at the trap, as hot water running through it constantly at dishwashing times tends to keep it clear. The amount of this hot water, however, is seldom enough to heat the waste pipe and melt grease at some distance from the trap.

Fat, grease and oil never should be discarded into a sink, lavatory or water closet. Fats, as well as hardened crusts scraped from cooking utensils, and leftover bits of food should be collected in cans that can be thrown away with garbage, Fig. 1. Remaining traces of grease should be wiped up with paper towels or napkins as in Fig. 2.

The most effective method of preventing stoppage from congealed grease and oil that

6

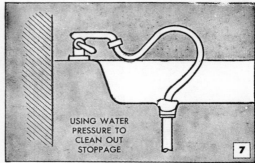

USING WATER
PRESSURE TO
CLEAN OUT
STOPPAGE

7

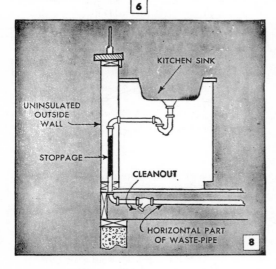

KITCHEN SINK

UNINSULATED
OUTSIDE
WALL

STOPPAGE

CLEANOUT

HORIZONTAL PART
OF WASTE-PIPE

8

are carried into a drain with dish water, is to run a copious amount of scalding water through the pipe for a period of at least 2 or 3 minutes after each dishwashing, Fig. 3. As soon as drainage through the pipe slows up, practically an entire tankful of scalding water should be run through it. The temperature control on the water heater should be set to "high" about an hour or so before such flushing.

Drain-pipe chemicals: If the scalding water treatment does not open up a slow drain, you can use a strong chemical cleaner. Most of these consist of sodium hydroxide (caustic soda), with bauxite and other ingredients added to intensify their action. Mixtures of caustic soda with sodium nitrate and aluminum turnings are also used, in which case ammonia gas is formed and dissolves the grease. The use of lye (caustic soda) alone frequently adds to the grease

accumulation more rapidly than it can be removed by water and then increases the stoppage. When added to water these chemicals effervesce violently and produce considerable heat.

As these drain-cleaning chemicals are extremely caustic they must be handled with care to avoid getting them or the solution on hands, arms and face. Also avoid splashing the chemical on clothes, wood, painted surfaces or aluminum. If this happens accidentally, flush with cold water, then immediately apply vinegar and finally rinse with cold water. After the chemical has been put in the drain pipe, do not use a plunger to hasten the removal of the grease accumulation. Keep water out of the can containing the chemical; if the content is wetted and the can lid is closed tightly, sufficient pressure may be produced inside to cause the can to "blow up."

A chemical cleaner should not be used in drain pipes that are completely clogged. It is necessary to have a slight flow to carry the chemical down to the point of obstruction, since it must be in contact with the obstruction to be effective. Pouring the chemical into a sink drain merely lets most of it settle in the trap. The best method is to remove the trap, as in Fig. 4, and insert the chemical in the pipe beyond the trap location as in Fig. 6. Use about a quarter of a full can and wash it down the pipe by slowly pouring in about a quart of water at intervals. Then replace the trap and after about 15 min. check to see if water drains away faster. Repeated chemical treatments are sometimes necessary. When good drainage is resumed, flush the pipe with scalding water for about 5 min.

Mechanical methods: When a sink or lavatory drain is completely stopped, mechanical methods must be employed usually to remove or pierce the obstruction. First try a suction-cup plunger, as in Fig. 5, a force pump, or use water pressure from a faucet, Fig. 7. In this case the hose must be securely attached to both faucet and sink drain. Be sure that there is enough water in the sink to provide a good seal when using a suction cup, and then work it up and down

9

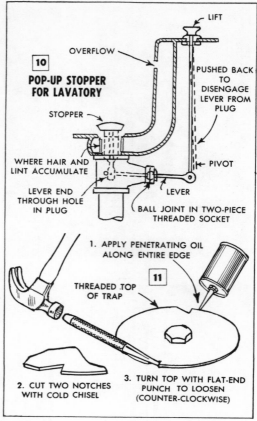

10

POP-UP STOPPER FOR LAVATORY

LIFT

OVERFLOW

PUSHED BACK TO DISENGAGE LEVER FROM PLUG

STOPPER

WHERE HAIR AND LINT ACCUMULATE

PIVOT

LEVER END THROUGH HOLE IN PLUG

LEVER

BALL JOINT IN TWO-PIECE THREADED SOCKET

1. APPLY PENETRATING OIL ALONG ENTIRE EDGE

11

THREADED TOP OF TRAP

2. CUT TWO NOTCHES WITH COLD CHISEL

3. TURN TOP WITH FLAT-END PUNCH TO LOOSEN (COUNTER-CLOCKWISE)

with quick, forcible strokes. These methods can be effective only when the obstruction lies between the sink and a vent pipe. If it lies beyond the vent pipe, air is admitted, which makes the suction cup ineffective. If water pressure is used, water will run up into the vent pipe instead of providing a positive pressure against the obstruction.

When these methods do not dislodge the obstruction, run a 15 to 25-ft. by ⅜-in. drain auger through the pipe, as in Fig. 9. Remove the trap and elbow from the pipe and feed the auger into it. Rotate it, then feed in farther and rotate again, continuing in this way until you have pierced the obstruction. If the latter cannot be reached conveniently from the sink location, open the cleanout plug at the beginning of the horizontal section and insert the auger at this point. It is impossible to remove all the grease from a pipe with an auger, but after a hole has been bored through the grease you apply the chemical treatment followed with a thorough flushing with scalding water.

An alternate method is to heat the pipe in order to melt the grease. You can use a blowtorch flame against the pipe if there is plenty of clearance between it and other inflammable material near it. An asbestos shield should be used to protect the latter from the flame.

Lavatory drains: Many lavatories have a pop-up type of drain stopper, Fig. 10, which tends to accumulate hair and lint just below the lavatory outlet. A length of wire having one end bent to a small hook can be used to pull out this accumulation, after removing the stopper. To do this you unscrew the ball-joint socket so that the short horizontal lever can be disengaged from the lower end of the stop plug. If the trap is clogged it may be cleared sometimes with a suction cup; in obstinate cases, it may have to be removed for cleaning.

Bath drains: Accumulations of lint, hair

and pieces of soap can cause clogging of bathtub and shower drains. Soap usually dissolves in a short time and passes away. When an accumulation clogs the trap and stops drainage flow, the cover of the trap must be removed, as in Fig. 11, to clean it. Turning the cover loose often can be made easier by letting some fine oil run over the edge of the cover and onto the threads. Tap the cover lightly while applying turning force. If it does not budge, chip two notches in the edge with a cold chisel and use a driving punch and hammer to turn the cover. When replacing it, be sure that the fiber gasket is thoroughly clean and in good condition. If defective, replace it rather than take a chance on admitting sewer gas. Putting a small amount of cup grease on the threads will make it easier to screw on the cover and will help also in getting a tight seal.

Water-closet stoppages: When a water-closet drain is stopped (usually paper causes this), try dislodging the obstruction with a suction cup first. If the suction cup is not effective, use a water-closet auger, although an ordinary drain auger can be employed. Often paper is caught by the spiral tip of the auger and can be pulled

12

PUTTY MOUND
AROUND OUTLET

THIN LAYER OF
PUTTY ON BASE

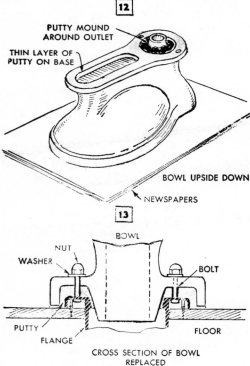

BOWL UPSIDE DOWN

NEWSPAPERS

13

BOWL

NUT

WASHER

BOLT

PUTTY

FLANGE

FLOOR

CROSS SECTION OF BOWL
REPLACED

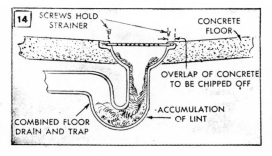

14 SCREWS HOLD
STRAINER

CONCRETE
FLOOR

OVERLAP OF CONCRETE
TO BE CHIPPED OFF

ACCUMULATION
OF LINT

COMBINED FLOOR
DRAIN AND TRAP

back. If a cake of soap is lodged in the trap, traces of it will show on the end of the auger. Soap is not easy to remove, but a quantity of hot water poured into the bowl will soften the soap and permit it to wash away.

Removing closet bowl: If the obstructing object cannot be removed with these methods, and it seems to be wedged in the trap, it will be necessary to remove the closet bowl to get at the obstruction from the outlet opening. First shut off the water supply and empty both the tank and the bowl by siphoning or pumping and sponging. Then disconnect the water-supply pipe to the tank, loosen the bolts holding the tank to the bowl if any, and also loosen the pipe connection between the tank and bowl, after which you can lift the tank off and carefully set it aside on newspapers. Some bowls can be removed without the need of removing the tank by only loosening the connection between the two. Next, remove the seat and loosen the bowl where it attaches to the floor, Fig. 12. Jar the bowl by hand to free it from the putty seal or gasket between the bowl and flange. Then lift off the bowl and set it upside down on newspapers. In this position the discharge opening is accessible.

Replacing closet bowl: Before replacing the bowl, clean away old putty from the base and flange. Dry the surfaces thoroughly and apply new bowl-setting putty to both bowl and flange, as shown in Fig. 13. About 3 lbs. of bowl-setting putty will be required; ordinary putty cannot be used. Build up a mound of putty around the outlet opening or "horn" of the bowl. Also apply a thin layer to the base where it contacts the floor, but keep the bolt holes clean. If a gasket is used instead of putty, replace it rather than take a chance on the old one. Contacting surfaces, in case a gasket is used, should be thoroughly clean. When replacing the bowl get it in exactly the same position as it was originally. Press it down to squeeze out the surplus putty and replace the nuts, tightening them carefully until the bowl rim is level. Then reconnect the tank if it was removed. If there is any water leakage from the puttied joint, take off the bowl again and reset with more putty. The bowl and tank should be handled with utmost care. They are made either of porcelain or vitreous china and can be chipped and scratched easily.

Floor drains: Floor sweepings and lint from washing clothes may cause floor drains to clog. Often the strainers, which are removable, are firmly held by the concrete floor which then must be chipped away a little in order to free them, Fig. 14. A long-handled spoon or ladle is handy to remove sediment from the trap, although

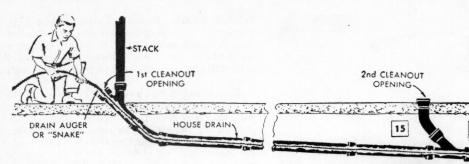

STACK
1st CLEANOUT OPENING
2nd CLEANOUT OPENING
DRAIN AUGER OR "SNAKE"
HOUSE DRAIN
15

a drain auger may be needed to loosen hard accumulations. When an opening has been made, you can apply water pressure from a garden hose to flush out the trap. If the trap is closed with congealed grease, first use a drain auger followed by a chemical drain cleaner and afterwards scalding water, as already explained. It is best to clean out floor drains periodically instead of waiting until they are completely stopped and the floor is covered with water.

Stoppages in house and storm drains: Where city sewers are not overtaxed and storm water from sewers does not back up into a house, the rise of water and sewage through floor drains indicates stoppage either in the house drain or in the house sewer. The cleanout, which usually is provided at the base of the soil stack, is the starting point for using a large drain auger or a spring-steel "snake" fitted with a spearhead. If drainage is restricted but is not entirely stopped, the obstruction can sometimes be flushed away by water pressure from a hose, in which case the nozzle is left on the hose and is adjusted for maximum force. If the obstruction is not found before reaching the cleanout opening at the outlet end, as in Fig. 15, you continue from this opening. When brass covers of cleanout openings are hard to remove, follow the same procedure of loosening them as explained for drum traps.

Where downspouts for roof drainage connect to storm or combination drains, soggy leaves sometimes cause obstructions, especially at turns. Remove the downspout and proceed with a drain auger until the mass of leaves has been loosened sufficiently to permit flushing them away with a hose. Leaf guards in gutters at downspout leaders avoid such trouble.

Root-filled house sewers: If the house drain is clear, but water from waste and drain pipes within the house causes flooding of the basement floor, the stoppage obviously must be in the house sewer or main sewer. This is reached through the cleanout opening which is closest to the outlet of the house drain. Penetration of tree roots into sewers is the most common cause of stoppage. Fig. 16 shows a section of pipe

16

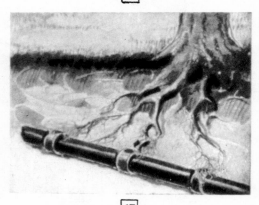

17

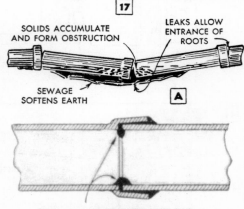

SOLIDS ACCUMULATE AND FORM OBSTRUCTION
LEAKS ALLOW ENTRANCE OF ROOTS
SEWAGE SOFTENS EARTH
A

B
MORTAR SQUEEZED INTO PIPE LIKELY TO START OBSTRUCTION

18

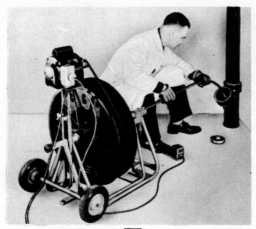

19

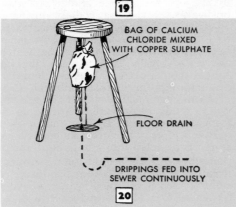

BAG OF CALCIUM
CHLORIDE MIXED
WITH COPPER SULPHATE

FLOOR DRAIN

DRIPPINGS FED INTO
SEWER CONTINUOUSLY

20

completely filled with tree roots. Some trees, particularly willows, poplars and cottonwoods, often send their roots out as far as 20 or 30 ft. in search of water. Slight cracks often found at mortar joints of pipe are enough to admit the hair ends of roots, Fig. 17. Once inside the pipe, roots grow fast and send out countless new roots. Any kind of pipe that has a leaky joint or a cracked wall is subject to root invasion. Other causes of stoppage in sewer lines are sagging sections of pipe in filled earth, as shown in Fig. 18A, mortar at joints that has gotten inside the pipe and was not wiped away, detail B, and filling up of broken pipes that have been crushed when not buried deeply enough, or have burst due to freezing.

Temporary control measures: The best tool for cutting roots inside a sewer pipe is an electrically driven root-cutting tool, shown in Fig. 19. Plumbers in localities that are especially subject to this trouble usually have such equipment. Cutting the roots and cleaning out the line, however, is only a temporary measure for immediate relief and does not prevent recurrence.

Other temporary control measures consist of applying some chemicals that kill or retard root growth. Repeated applications of caustic drain-cleaning chemicals retard root growth. Copper sulphate (blue vitriol) kills roots if applied in sufficient concentration over a period of time. One way to apply it continuously is to keep a strong solution in a container over a floor drain, arranging it so that the liquid will drip into the drain. The container can be provided with a petcock or with a suitable wick for slow, continuous dripping. Another dripping method, applicable where the air in a basement is sufficiently humid, is to mix copper sulphate and calcium chloride and hang the mixture in a porous bag over a floor drain, as in Fig. 20. The moisture retained by the calcium chloride dissolves the copper sulphate and drippings of both are fed into the sewer.

A single application of any chemical solution is not effective as it runs down the sewer and contacts the roots only momentarily. A 24-hr. or longer soaking application can be made if the house-sewer outlet can be plugged so that the solution will be retained in the line. However, as roots usually enter a sewer pipe through cracks at the bottom of joints where liquid is constantly available, the drip method is usually sufficient. Copper sulphate should not be introduced into a drain or sewer containing grease, as the chemical will coagulate the grease and form a nonsoluble substance that can cause further clogging. The application of chemicals should be greatest during spring and early summer months when root growth is rapid.

Replacing sewer pipe: The only permanent cure for root invasion is to seal the pipe joints so that roots cannot enter. If the pipe is not broken it is possible to enclose it completely in a layer of concrete as shown in Fig. 21, although the work and cost involved are no less than laying new pipe. Generally only a section of the line must be replaced, but while the job is being undertaken, it is often best to renew the entire line properly as assurance against future trouble.

Mortar joints of vitrified-clay pipe often are defective because of careless workmanship, although mortar joints properly made can be rootproof. Special pipe-joint compound, which is poured hot and remains slightly flexible, gives lasting protection when correctly applied. When replacing a section of vitrified-clay pipe, the damaged portion is broken up and removed, after which new pipe is laid. The joints are first calked, then sealed with pipe-joint compound. Fig. 22 shows how the two last sections of pipe can be fitted together so that the hub of one section need not be broken.

Other types of pipe are of value in preventing root invasion. On some types **the**

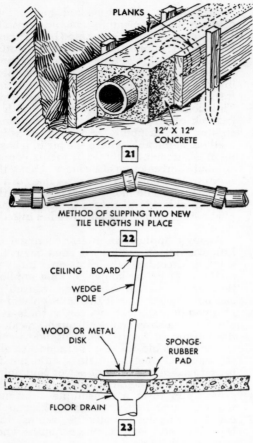

PLANKS

12" X 12"
CONCRETE

21

METHOD OF SLIPPING TWO NEW
TILE LENGTHS IN PLACE

22

CEILING BOARD

WEDGE
POLE

WOOD OR METAL
DISK

SPONGE-
RUBBER
PAD

FLOOR DRAIN

23

joints can be wedged together tightly in couplings; others have heavy-duty rubber-band seals that are forced between pipe ends and couplings. Cast-iron soil pipe with tightly leaded joints also gives adequate protection against root penetration.

Backflow from sewer: In localities where city sewers are overtaxed and occasionally cause sewage to back up into houses, the best remedy is to install a backflow valve. This is placed in the house drain. Temporary measures of preventing sewage from rising in basements through floor drains consist of sealing the drains with sponge-rubber disks held down tightly under wood or metal disks with a wedge stick, as in Fig. 23. In cases where the sewage may rise into a water closet located in the basement, the bowl must be plugged tightly in a similar or other effective manner.

Frozen drainage lines: A house sewer and other buried drainage lines should be below frost level to prevent freezing. Where this is impossible the lines should be insulated and the insulation wrapped in a moistureproof covering. Freezing of inside drainage lines can occur only when a house is left unheated, or when drainage lines are located in unheated spaces. Measures to prevent them from freezing should be taken when the lines are installed. When freezing does occur, the most effective measures to thaw out the frozen section depend on its location and accessibility.

In crawl spaces and other unheated places having sufficient room, a blowtorch can be used to heat the pipe if nearby wood and inflammable materials are protected with asbestos board. The flame must not be applied at joints of cast-iron soil pipe. This may melt the lead. Rags also may be wrapped around the pipe and kept soaked with hot water, or an electric heater can be set under the frozen section of pipe. After thawing the ice inside—or grease congealed by low temperature—it should be insulated to prevent recurrence and a quantity of hot water run through it daily during cold weather. If a crawl space is located next to a basement, an opening between the two can be made to admit some heat into the crawl space. In this case, the walls should be insulated. Vertical lengths of drainage pipe in outside walls can also be protected against freezing if the space between studs is provided with some heat from the basement. To thaw out a section of such a pipe, hot air from an electric heater-fan is directed into a basement opening.

Besides heating a pipe from the outside, it can also be heated from the inside. Assuming that it is full of water above the frozen section, it is best to run a hose or length of rubber tubing into the pipe and down to the obstruction so that the water can be pumped out. Then the pipe may be filled with scalding water, or chemicals may be introduced. A chemical cleaner which generates considerable heat can be flushed down to the obstruction. Another chemical that has been found effective is antifreeze of the kind used in auto gas tanks.

Protecting traps in unheated houses: Considerable damage in a drainage system can result by leaving water in traps and water closets in an unheated house when it is closed during cold weather. The water freezes and cracks the traps or closet bowls. Proper precautions to prevent this consist merely of removing all water from the traps and substituting a nonvolatile oil, such as kerosene, which will not congeal. Water is easily removed from washdown-type water closets by sponging out the trap. All siphon-jet water closets cannot be completely emptied in this manner. Those having a jet hole in the bottom of the bowl can be emptied by inserting a rubber tube through the hole and pumping out the water from the passage below the bowl. To protect water systems from frost, see *Water-System Troubles and Cures.*